A BLAST OF MATH

Grades 3-4

Written by Gunter Schymkiw
Published by World Teachers Press®

Published with the permission of R.I.C. Publications Pty. Ltd.

Copyright © 2001 by Didax, Inc., Rowley, MA 01969. All rights reserved.

First published by R.I.C. Publications Pty. Ltd., Perth, Western Australia. Revised by Didax Educational Resources.
 Cover this message when photocopying for student use.
Printed in the United States of America.

Order Number 2-5190
ISBN 1-58324-125-6

A B C D E F 03 02 01

Educational Resources
395 Main Street
Rowley, MA 01969
www.worldteacherspress.com

Foreword

The overall aim of the *A Blast of Math* series is to promote and develop mathematical discussion and student understanding of mathematical concepts within the classroom.

The *A Blast of Math* series features:

- precise mathematical explanations at both students' and teacher's levels
- a structured questioning layout to develop concepts sequentially and lead students to a logical answer
- strong support for the development of listening skills
- simple assessment of student understanding
- ease for the teacher to supply further information as required
- an ideal basis for further mathematical discussion
- an emphasis on student understanding rather than rote "correct" answers
- answers and explanations provided for quick and easy reference

The concept behind the series could not be easier; students are provided with a worksheet and teachers with an instruction/background sheet. Teachers are supplied with precise instructions to read out to the students, who respond by completing the appropriate section on their worksheet.

The publisher has chosen to use metric measurements for most activities in this book. The National Council of Teachers of Math supports the use of the metric system as an integral part of the mathematics curriculum at all levels of education (NCTM Position Statement on Metrication, 1986). In some activities, Imperial (English) measurements are used for illustrative purposes.

Other titles in the series are: *A Blast of Math* — Grades 4-5
A Blast of Math — Grades 5-6
A Blast of Math — Grades 6-7

Contents

Student progress chart   **Name** _____

Blast#	Date	Score	Comments/Errors
1		/20	
2		/20	
3		/20	
4		/20	
5		/20	
6		/20	
7		/20	
8		/20	
9		/20	
10		/20	
11		/20	
12		/20	
13		/20	
14		/20	
15		/20	
16		/20	
17		/20	
18		/20	
19		/20	
20		/20	
21		/20	
22		/20	
23		/20	
24		/20	
25		/20	
26		/20	
27		/20	
28		/20	
29		/20	

Teacher's notes

The activities contained in this series are wide and varied, and practice a range of general strategies students can use when dealing with mathematical problems across the curriculum. The activities promote a wide range of math concepts in addition to developing listening skills.

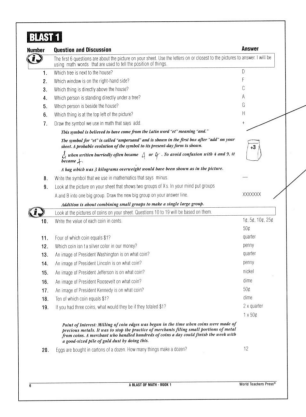

Extra information and explanations are included in italics.

Boxed information provides an explanation of the structure of the questioning and guides students to the relevant places on their worksheets.

Answer to each question provided here for easy reference.

Answers to extra activities provided where necessary.

Materials needed for the session are listed as needed.

Students answer all questions here.

Information and diagrams needed for questions are supplied on student worksheet.

Each activity is numbered clearly.

Extra activities have been added to consolidate work.

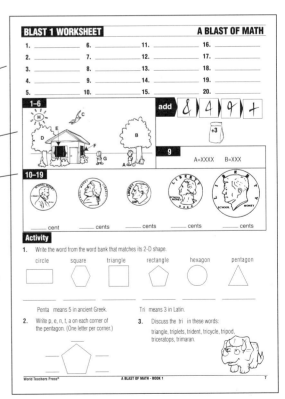

Number	Question and Discussion	Answer

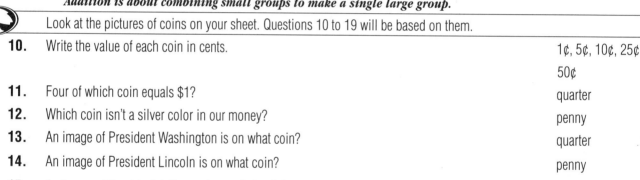

The first 6 questions are about the picture on your sheet. Use the letters on or closest to the pictures to answer. I will be using "math words" that are used to tell the position of things.

1. Which tree is next to the house? — D

2. Which window is on the right-hand side? — F

3. Which thing is directly above the house? — C

4. Which person is standing directly under a tree? — A

5. Which person is beside the house? — G

6. Which thing is at the top left of the picture? — H

7. Draw the symbol we use in math that says "add." — +

> *This symbol is believed to have come from the Latin word "et" meaning "and."*
>
> *The symbol for "et" is called "ampersand" and is shown in the first box after "add" on your sheet. A probable evolution of the symbol to its present-day form is shown.*
>
> *& when written hurriedly often became △ or ⅌ . To avoid confusion with 4 and 9, it became +.*
>
> *A bag which was 3 kilograms overweight would have been shown as in the picture.*

8. Write the symbol that we use in mathematics that says "minus." — −

9. Look at the picture on your sheet that shows two groups of X's. In your mind put groups

A and B into one big group. Draw the new big group on your answer line. — XXXXXXX

> *Addition is about combining small groups to make a single large group.*

Look at the pictures of coins on your sheet. Questions 10 to 19 will be based on them.

10. Write the value of each coin in cents. — 1¢, 5¢, 10¢, 25¢ 50¢

11. Four of which coin equals $1? — quarter

12. Which coin isn't a silver color in our money? — penny

13. An image of President Washington is on what coin? — quarter

14. An image of President Lincoln is on what coin? — penny

15. An image of President Jefferson is on what coin? — nickel

16. An image of President Roosevelt is on what coin? — dime

17. An image of President Kennedy is on what coin? — 50¢

18. Ten of which coin equals $1? — dime

19. If you had three coins, what would they be if they totaled $1? — 2 x quarter 1 x 50¢

> *Point of Interest: Milling of coin edges was begun in the time when coins were made of precious metals. It was to stop the practice of merchants filing small portions of metal from coins. A merchant who handled hundreds of coins a day could finish the week with a good-sized pile of gold dust by doing this.*

20. Eggs are bought in cartons of a dozen. How many things make a dozen? — 12

1. _____	6. _____	11. _____	16. _____
2. _____	7. _____	12. _____	17. _____
3. _____	8. _____	13. _____	18. _____
4. _____	9. _____	14. _____	19. _____
5. _____	10. _____	15. _____	20. _____

1–6

add ❯ 8 4 9 $+$

+3

9

A=XXXX   B=XXX

10–19

_____ cent   _____ cents   _____ cents   _____ cents   _____ cents

Activity

1. Write the word from the word bank that matches its 2-D shape.

circle   square   triangle   rectangle   hexagon   pentagon

_____   _____   _____   _____   _____   _____

"Penta" means 5 in ancient Greek.

"Tri" means 3 in Latin.

2. Write p, e, n, t, a on each corner of the pentagon. (One letter per corner.)

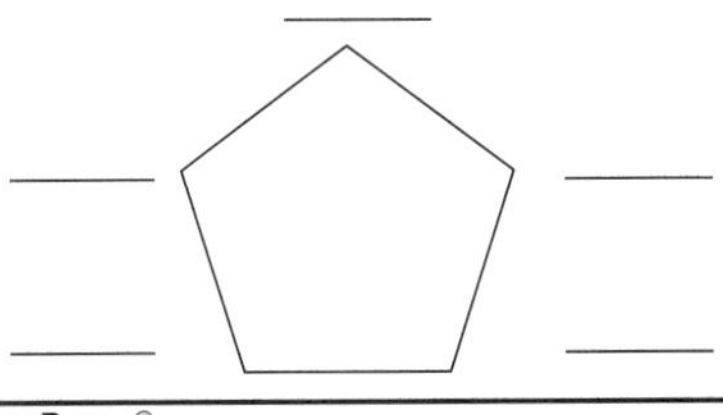

3. Discuss the "tri" in these words:

triangle, triplets, trident, tricycle, tripod, triceratops, trimaran.

BLAST 2

Number	Question and Discussion	Answer
ℹ️	Questions 1 to 4 are about the picture on your sheet showing a group of marbles.	
1.	If the colored marbles rolled away, how many marbles would be left behind?	3
2.	Write the number sentence that tells what happens if the colored marbles roll away.	$5 - 2 = 3$
	A number sentence is just like an ordinary sentence except it uses numbers to tell us something.	
3.	If no marbles rolled away, how many marbles would be left behind?	5
4.	Write the number sentence that tells what would happen if all the marbles rolled away.	$5 - 5 = 0$
ℹ️	Look at the picture on your sheet showing pieces of fruit. It is a picture graph showing the fruit eaten by Jim at a picnic. Each picture stands for one piece of fruit. Use the graph to answer questions 5 to 10.	
5.	How many apples did Jim eat?	3
6.	How many bananas did he eat?	1
7.	How many plums did he eat?	5
8.	How many pieces of fruit did he eat altogether?	9
9.	How many more apples did he eat than bananas?	2
10.	Which fruit did he probably like the best?	plums
	Statistics (numbers) can be misleading. Perhaps there was only one banana allowed per person. Perhaps he ate the plums first and was feeling full when he came to the apples, and so on.	
ℹ️	Abbreviations are short ways of writing things that are used often. On your sheet are some abbreviations you will be using a lot this year in math class. Use the abbreviations to complete the following.	
11.	Which abbreviation is short for "years"?	yrs
12.	Which abbreviation is short for "weeks"?	wks
13.	An hour is made up of 60 minutes. Write "60 minutes" using the abbreviation.	60 min.
14.	A minute is made up of 60 seconds. Write "60 seconds" using the abbreviation.	60 sec.
15.	A day is 24 hours long. Write "24 hours" using the abbreviation.	24 hrs
16.	There are 12 months in a year. Write "12 months" using the abbreviation.	12 mths
17.	Look at the picture showing 3 solid objects on your sheet. Which would roll most easily?	A
18.	Look at Barry, Gary and Clarrie. Who is tallest?	Barry
19.	Who is widest?	Clarrie
20.	Look at the pattern on your sheet. On answer line 20, draw the next 3 shapes in the pattern.	circle, triangle, square

Activity Answers

1. (a) 5   (b) 7   (c) 8   (d) 9   (e) 5   (f) 7   (g) 8   (h) 9

1. _____	6. _____	11. _____	16. _____
2. _____	7. _____	12. _____	17. _____
3. _____	8. _____	13. _____	18. _____
4. _____	9. _____	14. _____	19. _____
5. _____	10. _____	15. _____	20. _____

1–4

11–16

sec.   min.   hrs   wks   mths   yrs

5–10

apples

bananas

plums

17

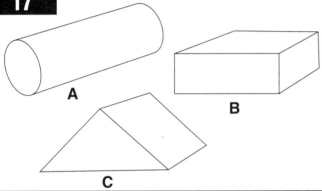

A

B

C

18–19

Gary   Barry   Clarrie

20

        ?

Activity

"Plus" means "add."

1. Read the questions, then write the answers.

(a) 3 plus 2 = _____
(b) 4 plus 3 = _____
(c) 6 plus 2 = _____
(d) 5 plus 4 = _____

(e) 2 plus 3 = _____
(f) 3 plus 4 = _____
(g) 2 plus 6 = _____
(h) 4 plus 5 = _____

What did you notice when you did these? _____

BLAST 3

Number	Question and Discussion	Answer

Sometimes words that are used a lot are written as abbreviations; an abbreviation is a shortened form of writing a word. The abbreviations for the days of the week are written on your sheet. Refer to them to answer questions 1 to 8.

Number	Question and Discussion	Answer
1.	What day is it today?	teacher
2.	What day was yesterday?	teacher
3.	What day will it be tomorrow?	teacher
4.	On which day does your class have social studies class?	teacher
5.	On which day does your class have gym class?	teacher
6.	Which day begins the weekend?	Sat.
7.	Which day is the first working day of the week?	Mon.
8.	What is the second day of the weekend?	Sun.
i	The next 2 questions relate to the number patterns A and B.	
9.	Write the next number in pattern A.	12
10.	Write the next number in pattern B.	11
11.	Look at your index finger. Using its length as a measure, how many times do you think it will fit along your arm from the elbow to the tip of your middle finger?	should be between 4 and 5 for most children
12.	Look at the meter stick I am holding up. Estimate the number of times it will fit (lengthways) across the blackboard.	teacher
i	On your sheet are more abbreviations for words we use to write how long things are. We call them measurements of "length." Use the abbreviations to write your answers for questions 13 to 15.	
13.	We measure things like lines in your book in "centimeters." Write the abbreviation for "centimeters."	cm
14.	A meter is 100 centimeters long. We use meters to measure a length like a park or football field. Write the abbreviation for meters.	m
15.	We measure the distance between towns or cities in kilometers. A kilometer is made up of a thousand meters. Write the abbreviation for kilometers.	km
i	Refer to the diagrams marked "A" and "B" to answer the next 2 questions.	
16.	Which diagram shows 2 sets of 3?	B
17.	Which diagram shows 3 sets of 2?	A
i	The last 3 questions are about Terry, Clarrie, Little Jessie and the seesaw.	
18.	Which side of the seesaw will go down if Terry sits at X and Clarrie sits at Y?	Y
19.	Which child probably has the greater "mass"?	Clarrie

Tell the children that the term "mass" is "math talk" for what they normally refer to as "weight." Although this is not a technically thorough definition of the term, it is one that will help children become familiar with the broad meaning of the term.

Number	Question and Discussion	Answer
20.	With whom might Terry be able to play on the seesaw without being in danger of being shot off into space?	Little Jessie

Additional Material Needed

Meter stick

1. _____
2. _____
3. _____
4. _____
5. _____

6. _____
7. _____
8. _____
9. _____
10. _____

11. _____
12. _____
13. _____
14. _____
15. _____

16. _____
17. _____
18. _____
19. _____
20. _____

1–8

Sat.   Sun.   Mon.   Tues.
Wed.   Thurs.   Fri.

9–10

A = 2, 4, 6, 8, 10   B = 1, 3, 5, 7, 9

13–15

cm   km   m

16–17

A = XX XX XX   B = XXX XXX

18–20

X   △   Y

Terry   Clarrie   Little Jessie

Activity

1. What day is the day before the day after yesterday?
   (Clue: use the list of days to work this out.)   _____

2. (a)   Color the shape with the largest surface area red.

   (b)   Color the shape with the smallest surface area blue.

   (c)   Color the shape that is medium-sized green.

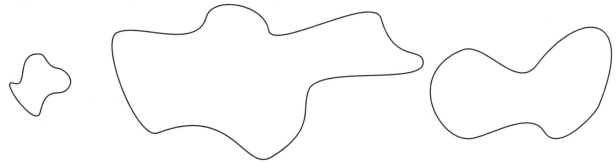

Number	Question and Discussion	Answer
	Remember that an abbreviation is the short form of writing terms that we use a lot. On your sheet there are three abbreviations that we use when writing the "mass" of things (how heavy things are). We measure the mass of something like an apple in "grams." A piece of apple might have a mass of 85 grams.	
1.	Write "85 grams" on answer line 1 using the abbreviation.	85 g
2.	You measure your own mass in kilograms. A child in your class might have a mass of 28 kilograms. Use the abbreviation to write "28 kilograms" on line 2.	28 kg
3.	The mass of large things like trucks or ships is measured in tons. A big truck might have a mass of 10 tons. Use the abbreviation to write "10 tons" on line 3.	10 t

ⓘ The next 3 questions are about the capacity of the 4 jelly jars on your sheet. "Capacity" means the amount of something they can hold. Use the letters below the jelly jars to answer these questions about capacity.

4.	Which jar will hold the most jelly (has the largest capacity)?	B
5.	Which jar has the smallest capacity?	C
6.	Which jar has the second biggest capacity?	D
7.	Look at your school ruler. It is marked off in intervals of 1 centimeter. Altogether it is 30 centimeters long (there may be exceptions). Look at your desk. Within 20 centimeters, estimate its height.	teacher

ⓘ Look at the line of shapes drawn on your sheet. You will be answering questions about this line using the "ordinal numbers" on your sheet. Ordinal numbers tell the order or place of things. The starting point of these questions is the far left and the end is at the far right.

8.	Which ordinal number describes the position of the blue checkmark?	2nd
9.	Which ordinal number tells the position of the red star?	5th
10.	Which ordinal number describes the position of the red triangle in the line?	7th
11.	What is the position of the red X in the line?	9th
12.	Which ordinal number describes the position of the red circle in the line?	3rd
13.	Write the ordinal number that tells the position of the red checkmark in this line.	1st
14.	Write the ordinal number that tells the position of the blue circle in the line.	4th
15.	Which ordinal number can be used to describe the position of the last thing in the line?	10th

Think of other places that ordinal numbers are used. (Position in a swimming or running race, gears on a car or bike, writing the date, presidents, etc.)

ⓘ The last 5 questions are about the letters and numbers on your sheet. Listen to the number stories. When you have worked out an answer, write the letter that matches it.

16.	There were 4 sheep in a pen and 2 went to the movies. How many were left in the pen? Write the letter that matches your answer.	M
17.	10 minus 7 equals? Write the letter that matches your answer.	I
18.	There were 10 birds in a tree. A barking dog scared 4 away. How many birds were left in the tree? Write the letter that matches your answer.	N
19.	I had 10 grapes but ate 5. How many were left? Write the letter that matches your answer.	U
20.	If 6 people were on a bus and 2 got off at the first stop, how many were left on the bus? Write the letter that matches your answer.	S

Note that answers spell the word "minus." This is a "math word" used for subtraction. All the stories needed you to subtract to get your answer.

Additional Material Needed

Children need meter sticks

Activity Answers

1. (a) Apr.   (b) Feb.   (c) Jul.   (d) Jun.   (e) Feb.   (f) Jan.   (g) Dec.

1. _____	6. _____	11. _____	16. _____
2. _____	7. _____	12. _____	17. _____
3. _____	8. _____	13. _____	18. _____
4. _____	9. _____	14. _____	19. _____
5. _____	10. _____	15. _____	20. _____

1–3

The abbreviations below are used when measuring "**mass.**"

kg   g   t

4–6

A   B   C   D

8–15

✔	✔	●	●	☆	☆	▲	▲	✘	✘
red	blue	red	blue	red	blue	red	blue	red	blue
1st	2nd	3rd	4th	5th	6th	7th	8th	9th	10th

16–20

1=E	2=M	3=I	4=S	5=U	6=N	7=T

Activity

1. The abbreviations for the months are shown below. They are not written in correct calendar order. Use the abbreviations to answer the questions below.

May   Jul.   Feb.   Jan.   Jun.   Dec.   Mar.   Sept.   Oct.   Nov.   Apr.   Aug.

(a)   Which is the 4th month of the year?   _____

(b)   Which month follows January?   _____

(c)   Which is the 7th month of the year?   _____

(d)   Which month comes immediately before July?   _____

(e)   Which is the shortest month of the year?   _____

(f)   Which month begins the year?   _____

(g)   Which month ends the year?   _____

Number	Question and Discussion	Answer
(i)	Questions 1 to 5 relate to the picture on your sheet showing a line of shapes. Draw the shapes to answer the questions. The questions all use words that tell us the position of things.	
1.	Draw the shape that is in the "middle."	A
2.	Draw the shape on the "far right."	triangle
3.	Draw the shape on the "far left."	star
4.	Draw the shape "second from the end on the right."	square
5.	Draw the shape that is "2 to the left of the middle."	circle
	Show children the meter stick.	
6.	Estimate the distance across the classroom.	teacher
(i)	Questions 7 to 12 are about the pictures that represent 3-D shapes. "3-D" is the short way of writing "three-dimensional."	
	Ask the children to stand. Ask them to move from side to side and tell them that this is one dimension. Ask them to jump up and down and tell them that this is another dimension. Finally ask them to move backwards and forwards and tell them that this is the third dimension.	
7.	Which picture represents a "rectangular prism"?	E
8.	Which picture represents a "sphere"?	C
9.	Which picture represents a "cylinder"?	A
10.	Which picture represents a "cube"?	D
11.	Which picture represents a "cone"?	B
12.	Which picture represents a "pyramid"?	F
(i)	Choose the words that we use to describe temperature when answering the next 4 questions.	
13.	Which word describes the temperature of an ice cube?	cold
14.	Which word describes the temperature of a glass of drinking water from the faucet?	cool
15.	Which word describes the temperature of a piece of toast 1 minute after it has been taken out of the toaster?	warm
16.	Which word describes the temperature of the water in a saucepan 2 seconds after it has begun to boil?	hot
(i)	Refer to the groups X and Y to answer the next 3 questions.	
17.	Which diagram shows 2 sets of 4?	Y
	A "number sentence" is just like a sentence made up of words, except that it uses numbers and symbols to tell us something.	
18.	Write the "sets of" number sentence that X shows.	4 x 2 = 8
19.	Write an addition number sentence for Y.	4 + 4 = 8
20.	Circle groups of 10 bees in the swarm on your sheet. Count the number of groups of ten and the ones left over, then write the number of bees in the swarm.	27

Additional Material Needed

Meter stick

1. _____	6. _____	11. _____	16. _____
2. _____	7. _____	12. _____	17. _____
3. _____	8. _____	13. _____	18. _____
4. _____	9. _____	14. _____	19. _____
5. _____	10. _____	15. _____	20. _____

1–5

☆ ○ ✔ A ✕ □ △

7–12

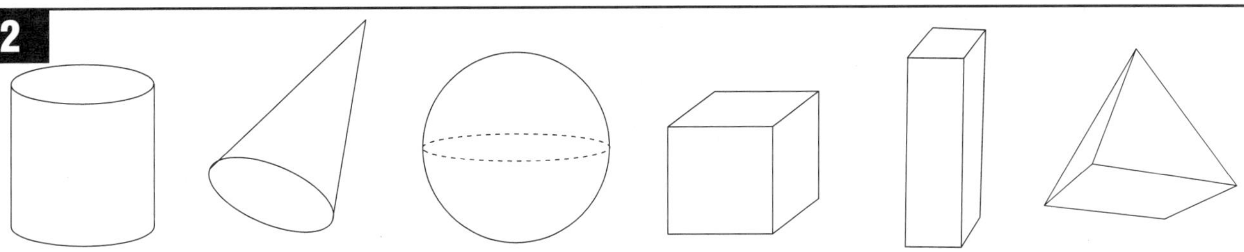

A   B   C   D   E   F

13–16

cool	hot
warm	cold

17–19

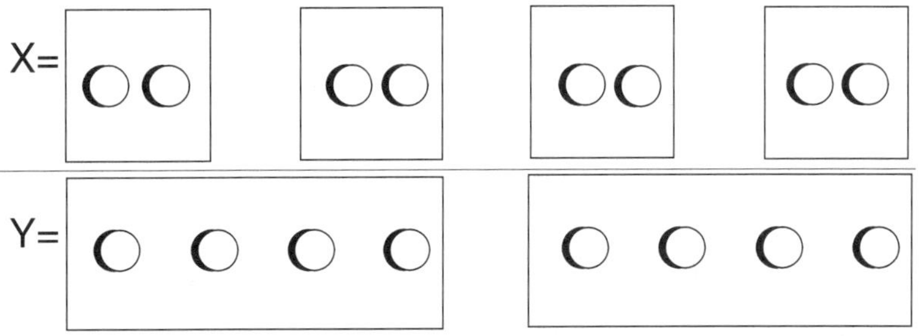

$X=$ ○○   ○○   ○○   ○○

$Y=$ ○ ○ ○ ○   ○ ○ ○ ○

A number sentence uses numbers instead of words.

20

Activity

1. Match the 3-D shape names to the pictures.

cylinder   cone   sphere   cube   rectangular prism   square pyramid

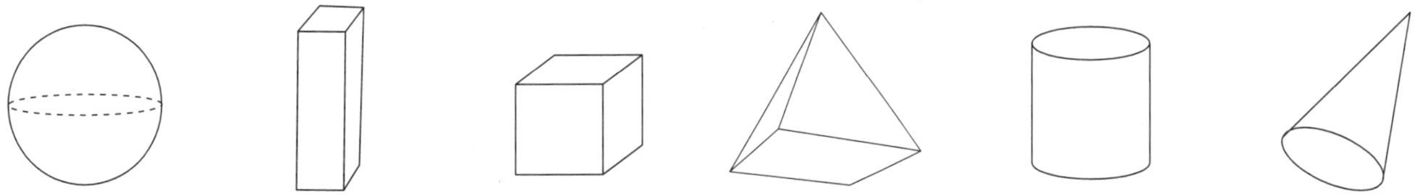

BLAST 6

Number	Question and Discussion	Answer
	Questions 1 to 8 can be answered using the abbreviations written on your sheet.	
1.	We measure the length of some things in centimeters. A school ruler is usually 30 cm long. Add the abbreviation for centimeters to the 30 on answer line one.	30 cm
2.	We measure some things in meters. A doorway in your house is about 2 meters high. Write 2 meters using the abbreviation.	2 m
3.	Kilometers are used to measure greater lengths like the distances between towns. The distance between Birmingham, Alabama and Atlanta, Georgia is about 150 kilometers. Add the abbreviation to the answer line so that it says 150 kilometers.	150 km
4.	Grams are used to measure small masses (weights). A can of peaches has a mass of 825 grams. Add the abbreviation to the answer on the line.	825 g
5.	A person's mass is recorded in kilograms. A child in our class might have a mass of 34 kilograms. Write this using the abbreviation.	34 kg
6.	The masses of large things like cars, trucks, trains, or ships are usually recorded in tons. A blue whale has a mass of about 150 tons. Add the abbreviation on the line so that it says 150 tons.	150 t
7.	Liquids like fruit juice are often measured in milliliters. A fruit juice container holds about 250 milliliters. Add the abbreviation to the 250 on your answer line so that it says 250 milliliters.	250 mL
	Note the small "m" and capital "L."	
8.	Larger amounts of liquid are recorded in liters. A plastic bucket holds about 10 liters of water. Write 10 liters using the abbreviation.	10 L
	Note the capital "L."	
9.	Within 10 centimeters, estimate how many centimeters from the front to the back of your desk.	teacher
10.	Look at the swarm of bees on your sheet. Circle groups of ten. How many groups are there?	3
11.	How many bees are there altogether?	36
12.	How many ones are there?	6
	Choose the correct word from the 2 on your sheet to answer the next 2 questions.	
13.	In which direction is the bicycle wheel moving?	clockwise
14.	In which direction is the hoop moving?	counter-clockwise
15.	Mary's story is very long. She has filled both sides of 7 sheets of paper and one side on an 8th sheet of paper. How many pages long is her story?	15
	The next questions relate to the pictures of coins on your sheet. Some of the coins are in circulation (use) now. Some were once in circulation (use), but aren't any longer, and some have never been coins in our currency.	
16.	Write the smallest value coin currently in circulation.	1¢
17.	Write the highest value coin currently in circulation.	$1
	We measure the temperature of things in degrees Celsius. The abbreviation for degrees Celsius is shown on answer lines 18 and 19.	
18.	Water boils at 100 degrees Celsius. Write 100 in front of the abbreviation to see what this temperature looks like when written down.	100°C
19.	Water freezes at zero degrees Celsius. Put a zero in front of the abbreviation to see what this looks like.	0°C
20.	Close your eyes and estimate, to the nearest five seconds, the number of seconds between when I say "start" and "stop."	teacher
	Allow the stopwatch to run for 20 seconds. Discuss ways of counting in 1-second intervals.	

Additional Material Needed

Stopwatch

Activity Answers

1. (a) 38   (b) 62

A BLAST OF MATH - BOOK 1   World Teachers Press®

1. __30__   6. __150__   11. _____   16. _____

2. _____   7. __250__   12. _____   17. _____

3. __150__   8. _____   13. _____   18. _____ °C

4. __825__   9. _____   14. _____   19. _____ °C

5. _____   10. _____   15. _____   20. _____

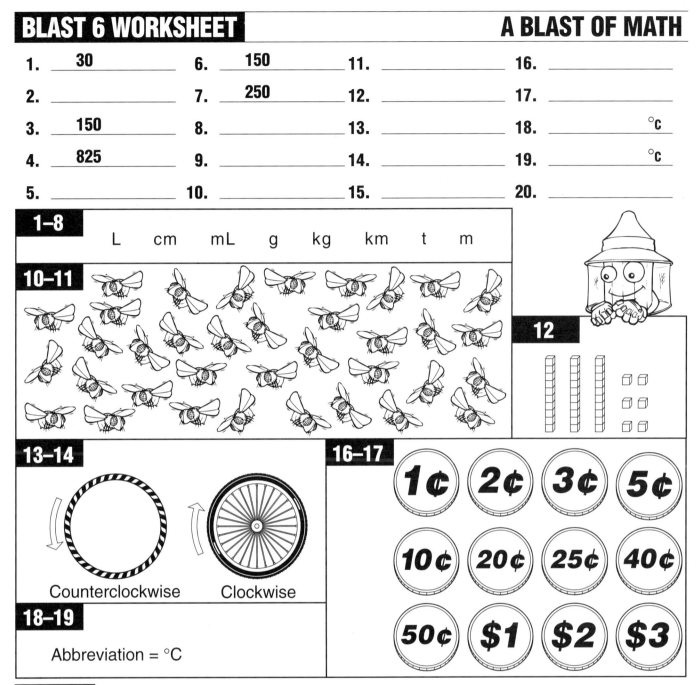

1–8

L   cm   mL   g   kg   km   t   m

10–11

12

13–14

Counterclockwise   Clockwise

18–19

Abbreviation = °C

16–17

1¢ 2¢ 3¢ 5¢
10¢ 20¢ 25¢ 40¢
50¢ $1 $2 $3

Activity

Place Value

1. Each bundle has 10 pencils in it. Write the number of pencils shown altogether in each group.

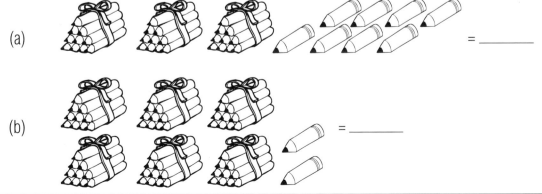

(a)   = _____

(b)   = _____

Number	Question and Discussion	Answer
	Look at the capital letters on your sheet. Refer to them when answering questions 1 to 3.	
1.	On answer line 1, write any 2 letters that are "closed shapes."	A, B, D, O, P, Q, R
2.	Now write any two letters that are not closed shapes on answer line 2.	C, E, F, G, H, I, J, K, L, M, N, S, T, U, V, W, X, Y, Z
3.	Look at the letter on answer line 3. Add a line to it so that it is turned into a closed shape.	▽
4.	Look at how 5¢ and 10¢ are written using the dollar sign. Copy them on answer line 4.	$0.05, $0.10
5.	Write one cent as dollars and cents.	$0.01
	Questions 6 to 9 relate to the diagrams of the groups X and Y on your sheet.	
6.	Which picture shows 5 groups of 2?	Y
7.	Write the "sets of" number sentence shown by X.	2 x 5 = 10
8.	Write the addition number sentence shown by X.	5 + 5 = 10
9.	Write the "sets of" number sentence for Y.	5 x 2 = 10
10.	Close your eyes and count to estimate the number of seconds between when I say "start" and "stop." Your answer should end in 0 or 5. *Allow the stopwatch to run for 35 seconds.*	teacher
11.	A videotape runs for one hour. How many minutes is this?	60 min.
	Questions 12 to 15 are about "symmetry." If a line cuts a shape so that one half is an exact reflection of the other, the shape is said to have "symmetry" (or be "symmetrical"). Write "S" for "symmetrical" or "NS" for "not symmetrical" when answering the questions.	
12.	Write S or NS for the face, using the dotted line as a line of symmetry.	S
13.	Write S or NS for the apple labeled A, using the dotted line as a line of symmetry.	NS
14.	Write S or NS for the apple labeled B, using the dotted line as a line of symmetry.	S
15.	Look at your hand with the palm facing you. Is it symmetrical or not symmetrical? Write S or NS.	NS
	The last 5 questions are about the seasons written on your sheet.	
16.	Which season comes immediately before spring?	winter
17.	Which season follows immediately after summer?	fall
18.	Which season follows immediately after winter?	spring
19.	In which season do most people go to the beach or pool?	summer
20.	Which season is it now?	teacher

Additional Material Needed

Stopwatch

1. _____   6. _____   11. _____   16. _____

2. _____   7. _____   12. _____   17. _____

3. _____   8. _____   13. _____   18. _____

4. _____   9. _____   14. _____   19. _____

5. _____   10. _____   15. _____   20. _____

1–3

A B C D E F G H I J K L M N O P Q R S T U V W X Y Z

4–5

5¢ = $0.05

10¢ = $0.10

6–9

X =

Y =

12–15

S = symmetrical   NS = not symmetrical

   (a) 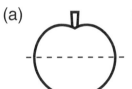   (b)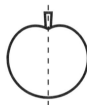

16–20

spring   summer   fall   winter

Activity

1. Color the seasons wheel on your sheet. Choose colors that you think match each season. Begin at "Spring" and go in a clockwise direction.

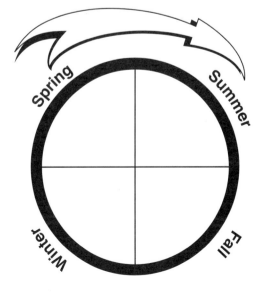

BLAST 8

Number	Question and Discussion	Answer
1.	Within 10 centimeters, estimate how far it is across your worksheet.	teacher
2.	Choose one of the times written in abbreviated form on your sheet to answer this question. About how long might it take you to count aloud to 100 (by ones)?	About 1 min.

(i) Questions 3 to 9 relate to the letters and numbers on your sheet. When you have worked out the answer, write the letter that matches it on your answer line. You may use the number ladder.

3.	Jim had 8 marbles. He won 7 more playing with his friends. How many did he have altogether? Write the letter that matches your answer.	R
4.	Mike did 2 push-ups every morning for a week. How many push-ups did he do in that week? Write the letter that matches your answer.	O
5.	In a basketball game, Mia scored 15 points. Tammy scored 2 points less than Mia. How many points did Tammy score? Write the letter that matches your answer.	Y
6.	Tahnee made 14 mud pies. She sold 2 at her pie and lemonade stall. How many did she have left? Write the letter that matches your answer.	G
7.	Superchimp had 16 bananas. He ate 5. How many did he have left? Write the letter that matches your answer.	B
8.	One spider has 8 legs. How many legs do 2 spiders have? Write the letter that matches your answer.	I
9.	Seven fleas were watching a football game on television. Twelve more joined them. How many were watching now? Write the letter that matches your answer.	V

Note that the letters spell the acronym ROY G BIV which can be used to remember the colors of the rainbow; red, orange, yellow, green, blue, indigo, violet.

10.	Estimate how far it is from the front of the classroom to the back.	teacher

(i) Use the hundreds chart to work out answers 11 to 14.

11.	In a multiplication test, Ron made 7 mistakes out of 100. What number did he get right?	93
12.	One hundred children went on a field trip. Three became sick and had to go home early. How many were left?	97
13.	Mary made only 4 spelling mistakes in a test of 100 words. How many did she spell correctly?	96
14.	Terry has 100 stamps. He used 6 to mail a package. How many does he have left?	94

(i) The next question refers to the diagram showing the groups S and T on your sheet.

15.	How many have to be added to group T to make it have the same number of members as group S?	2

This can be used to demonstrate the concept of "difference." The "difference" in mathematics is the answer you get when you subtract. Subtraction answers can be found in a number of ways. Sometimes we "count backward": 4–1, count back 1 from 4 to get the answer 3. Sometimes we "count forward": 4–1, count forward from 1 until you reach 4.

(i) The bags in the pictures on your sheet are supposed to hold 20 kilograms of wheat. When Ginny weighed them, she found that they were all underweight and she marked them accordingly. Use the number ladder to work out the answers if you need to.

16.	Bag X weighed 3 kilograms too little. How many kilograms of wheat did it contain?	17 kg
17.	Bag Y weighed 7 kilograms too little. How many kilograms of wheat did it contain?	13 kg
18.	Look bag Z. How many kilograms of wheat did it contain?	8 kg

Choose a child from the class.

19.	Estimate this person's height.	teacher
20.	Estimate my height.	teacher

Additional Material Needed

School ruler, meter stick, you may want to draw a number ladder to 20 on the board to demonstrate its use ("up" for "add" and "down" for "subtract"), a hundreds chart would be useful to demonstrate the working of questions 11–14. something to measure a child's height.

1. _____	6. _____	11. _____	16. _____
2. _____	7. _____	12. _____	17. _____
3. _____	8. _____	13. _____	18. _____
4. _____	9. _____	14. _____	19. _____
5. _____	10. _____	15. _____	20. _____

Number ladder

| 1 |
| 2 |
| 3 |
| 4 |
| 5 |
| 6 |
| 7 |
| 8 |
| 9 |
| 10 |
| 11 |
| 12 |
| 13 |
| 14 |
| 15 |
| 16 |
| 17 |
| 18 |
| 19 |
| 20 |

Hundreds chart

1	2	3	4	5	6	7	8	9	10
11	12	13	14	15	16	17	18	19	20
21	22	23	24	25	26	27	28	29	30
31	32	33	34	35	36	37	38	39	40
41	42	43	44	45	46	47	48	49	50
51	52	53	54	55	56	57	58	59	60
61	62	63	64	65	66	67	68	69	70
71	72	73	74	75	76	77	78	79	80
81	82	83	84	85	86	87	88	89	90
91	92	93	94	95	96	97	98	99	100

2

1 min.   1 hr   1 sec.

3–9

B = 11	G = 12
Y = 13	O = 14
R = 15	I = 16
V = 19	

15

S = | X | X | X |

T = | X |

16–18

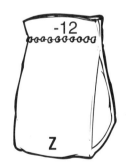

Activity

1. Color the months of spring yellow, summer red, autumn green and winter blue.

December	June	March	September
January	July	April	October
February	August	May	November

Number	Question and Discussion	Answer
(i)	Refer to the letters and numbers on your sheet. When you have worked out the answer, write the letter that matches it. You may use the number line to help you find the answer.	
1.	Sonya had 7 toys. She was given 3 more for her birthday. How many did she have altogether? Write the letter that matches your answer.	A
2.	Stan has 10 pencils in his pencil case and 4 on his desk. How many pencils does he have altogether? Write the letter that matches your answer.	D
3.	Stella has 9 stickers in her math book and 5 in her vocabulary book. How many stickers does she have altogether? Write the letter that matches your answer.	D
4.	In three volleyball games, Blanche scored 6 points, 4 points and 10 points. How many points did she score altogether in the three games? Write the letter that matches your answer.	I
5.	Renee's softball team won their game by 12 runs to 4. How many runs were scored altogether in the game? Write the letter that matches your answer.	T
6.	Joanna has read 12 pages of her book. She has 8 more to read to finish the book. How many pages are in the book? Write the letter that matches your answer.	I
7.	Peter's hens laid 11 eggs on Saturday and 7 on Sunday. How many did they lay altogether on that weekend? Write the letter that matches your answer.	O
8.	Richard has peeled 9 potatoes. He still has 8 more to peel. How many potatoes is this altogether?	N
	Note that the letters spell "ADDITION." All the problems were addition problems.	
9.	Close your eyes and count to estimate the number of seconds between when I say "start" and "stop." Your answer should end in 0 or 5.	teacher
	Allow the stopwatch to run for 60 seconds.	
10.	Choose a child from the class. Ask the children to estimate the child's height.	teacher
11.	Estimate the height of the doorway.	teacher
12.	Within 10 degrees Celsius, estimate the temperature in the classroom right now. Write the "degrees Celsius" abbreviation as part of your answer.	teacher
(i)	Questions 13 to 17 relate to the picture showing a line of children going into a building. Listen to the "position words," then write your answer.	
13.	Who is at the **end** of the line?	E
14.	Who is **immediately in front of** the boy standing on his head?	B
15.	Who is immediately **behind** the boy standing on his head?	D
16.	Which thing is **furthest left** in the picture?	S
17.	Which bird is **above** the children but **below** the cloud?	X
(i)	Write the correct notation from the box to answer questions 18 to 20.	
	Because we don't use these symbols very often it is easy to get them mixed up. It helps if we can come up with a "memory trick" to help us remember what they say. "<" could be thought of as an "L" leaning over ("L" for "Less than"). For the number sentence to be correct, the larger end of the symbol should be facing the larger number.	
18.	Which one applies to the mass of a pencil?	< 1 kg
19.	Which applies to the mass of a third-grader?	> 1 kg
20.	Which applies to the mass of a feather?	< 1 kg

Additional Material Needed

Stopwatch, something to measure a child's height, room thermometer

Activity Answers

1. (a) triangular prism – 5 faces (b) square prism – 6 faces (c) hexagonal prism – 8 faces (d) pentagonal prism – 7 faces
2. Number of faces is 2 more than number of corners in the "naming face."

1. _____	6. _____	11. _____	16. _____
2. _____	7. _____	12. _____	17. _____
3. _____	8. _____	13. _____	18. _____
4. _____	9. _____	14. _____	19. _____
5. _____	10. _____	15. _____	20. _____

1–8

1	2	3	4	5	6	7	8	9	10	11	12	13	14	15	16	17	18	19	20

B = 8   A = 10   D = 14   S = 15   T = 16   N = 17   O = 18   I = 20

12

°C

18–20

>1kg   <1kg

13–17

Activity

Prisms

1. The pictures below represent prisms. Choose from the word bank to name each prism, then write the number of faces it has. The face with a letter on it is known as the "naming face."

2. Can you see a pattern in the number of faces a prism has?

_____

square prism	triangular prism	hexagonal prism	pentagonal prism

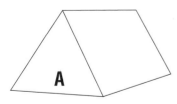 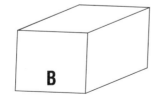 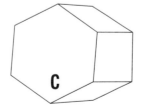 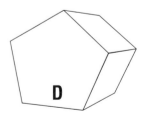

_____ _____ _____ _____

_____ _____ _____ _____

faces = _____ faces = _____ faces = _____ faces = _____

BLAST 10

Number	Question and Discussion	Answer
	The first 3 questions relate to the pictures that represent solid shapes on your sheet.	
1.	Which has 2 round faces and a curved surface?	C
2.	Which has 1 curved surface and a round face?	A
3.	Which has 1 curved surface?	B
	Questions 4 to 11 relate to the letters and numbers on your sheet. When you have worked out the answers, write the letters that match them. Use the number line if you need to.	
4.	Rover had 11 bones. He gave 8 to Fido. How many bones did Rover have left? Write the letter that matches your answer.	S
5.	Bob Bulldog was given 9 rubber balls on his birthday. He chewed up 5. How many did he have left? Write the letter that matches your answer.	U
6.	Jazmin's book has 10 pages in it. She has read 5. How many more does she have to read? Write the letter that matches your answer.	B
7.	Chris has 11 pencils. Only 5 are sharp. How many does he have to sharpen? Write the letter that matches your answer.	T
8.	There were 10 apples on a tree. On a windy day 3 were blown down. How many were still on the tree? Write the letter that matches your answer.	R
9.	There are 8 boys and 7 girls in a class. What is the **difference** in numbers between boys and girls? Write the letter that matches your answer.	A
10.	Miriam has done 8 of the 10 questions in a math test. How many does she have to do to finish the test? Write the letter that matches your answer.	C
11.	Craig was supposed to draw a 7-cm line in his book. He drew one that was 13 cm long instead. How many centimeters did he have to erase? Write the letter that matches your answer.	T
	Note the answers spell "SUBTRACT." All the questions involved "subtracting." "Difference" in mathematics can be found by subtracting.	
12.	Write "3 sets of 5" as an addition number sentence.	$5 + 5 + 5 = 15$
13.	Close your eyes and count to estimate the number of seconds between when I say "start" and "stop."	teacher
	Tell the children that the answer will end in 0 or 5. Allow the stopwatch to run for 70 seconds.	
14.	Look at the "long date" written on your sheet. Write this date in "short form."	5-20-2005, or 5/20/2005
15.	Which is the shortest month? Use its abbreviation to write your answer.	Feb.
16.	Within 10 degrees Celsius, estimate the temperature in the classroom right now. Write the "degrees Celsius" abbreviation as part of your answer.	teacher
17.	How many days are there in two weeks?	14
	Choose the correct word from the page to describe the part of a 3-D shape.	
18.	Is Tom painting a face, edge, or corner of his giant shoebox?	face
19.	Has Andy Ant come to a face, edge, or corner of the shoebox?	edge
20.	Is Lily about to step on a face, edge, or corner of the pyramid?	corner

Additional Material Needed

Stopwatch, room thermometer

1. _____   6. _____   11. _____   16. _____

2. _____   7. _____   12. _____   17. _____

3. _____   8. _____   13. _____   18. _____

4. _____   9. _____   14. _____   19. _____

5. _____   10. _____   15. _____   20. _____

1–3

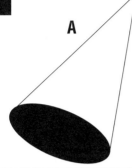 A

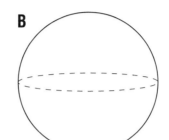 B

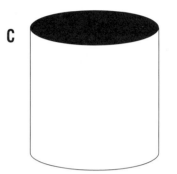 C

4–11

1	2	3	4	5	6	7	8	9	10	11	12	13	14	15	16	17	18	19	20

A = 1   C = 2   S = 3   U = 4   B = 5

T = 6   R = 7   D = 8   E = 9

14

May 20, 2005

18–20

      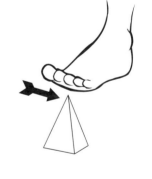

corner   edge   face

Activity

1.   Write the missing short dates.

Long Date	Short Date
September 14, 2001	9/14/2001
April 25, 1915	
July 3, 2010	
January 1, 1901	

Number	Question and Discussion	Answer
	Choose from these names to answer questions 1 to 3.	
1.	Which shape is the same as a shoebox?	rectangular prism
2.	Which shape is like a wizard's hat?	cone
3.	Which shape is like a jelly jar?	cylinder
	The diagram on your sheet represents an overhead view of the classroom. Refer to it to answer the next 5 questions.	
4.	In approximately which section do you sit?	teacher
5.	Write the initials of someone who sits in A.	teacher
6.	Write the initials of someone who sits in B.	teacher
7.	Write the initials of someone who sits in C.	teacher
8.	Write the initials of someone who sits in D.	teacher
	Choose a child from the class.	
9.	Estimate this person's height.	teacher
10.	Estimate the height of your desk.	teacher
	Look at the descriptions of length on your sheet. Use the letters to answer the next 3 questions.	
11.	Which best describes the width of the classroom door?	teacher
12.	Which most closely describes the length of a school pencil?	C
13.	Which best describes the height of a telephone pole?	B
	The next 3 questions are about the lines X, Y and Z and the words used to describe them.	
14.	Horizontal lines run the same way as the horizon. Which line is horizontal?	Z
15.	Telephone poles are vertical. Which line is vertical?	X
16.	Which line is oblique? ("Oblique" means slanting or sloping.)	Y
	The last 4 questions are about the clocks. Clock A currently shows the time as 9 o'clock.	
17.	For Clock A, to which number is the "minute hand" pointing?	12
18.	Where will the minute hand point at half past nine?	6
19.	Which clock shows 10 o'clock?	C
20.	Which clock shows 5 o'clock?	E

Additional Material Needed

Something to measure child's height

Activity Answers

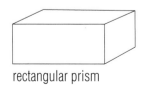

rectangular prism

cone

cylinder

1. _____	6. _____	11. _____	16. _____
2. _____	7. _____	12. _____	17. _____
3. _____	8. _____	13. _____	18. _____
4. _____	9. _____	14. _____	19. _____
5. _____	10. _____	15. _____	20. _____

1–3

cylinder   rectangular prism   cone

4–8

front

| A | B |
| C | D |

back

11–13

A = about 1 meter

B = longer than a meter

C = shorter than a meter

14–16

horizontal

vertical

oblique

X   Y   Z

17–20

A   B   C   D   E

Activity

1. Match the 3-D shape names to the shapes.

cylinder   rectangular prism   cone

BLAST 12

Number	Question and Discussion	Answer
ⓘ	Questions 1 to 8 relate to the picture graph on your sheet. It shows information (data) about the toys in a toy store. Each box stands for 1 of that kind of toy.	
1.	How many toy boats are in the store?	4
2.	How many trumpets are in the store?	1
3.	How many toy cars are in the store?	3
4.	How many dolls are in the store?	5
5.	How many balls are in the store?	6
6.	How many more dolls are there than trumpets?	4
7.	How many fewer ships are there than dolls?	1
8.	How many toys are there altogether in this survey?	19
ⓘ	The next 3 questions relate to the names of solid shapes on your sheet.	
9.	Which shapes are a pair of dice?	cube
10.	Which shape is the Earth?	sphere
11.	Which shape looks like the roof of some houses?	square pyramid
	Choose a child from the class.	
12.	Estimate this person's height.	teacher
13.	Estimate the height of my desk.	teacher
14.	Within 10 degrees Celsius, estimate the temperature in the classroom right now. Write the "degrees Celsius" abbreviation as part of your answer.	teacher
ⓘ	The next 2 questions are about "**perimeter**."	
	This is a "math word" that means "the distance around the outside of something." The word comes from two words from the language spoken in Greece thousands of years ago. The first part, "peri" means "around." The second part comes from the word "metron," meaning "measure." Another "peri" word is "periscope." The "scope" part comes from another old Greek word meaning "to watch." So a "periscope" is used to watch (or look) around.	
15.	Which rectangle has the shorter perimeter?	A
16.	What is the perimeter of B?	22 units
ⓘ	The next 4 questions are about telling the time on an analog clock. If you can count by 5s you can tell the time on an analog clock.	
17.	To which numeral does the minute (big) hand point at 20 minutes past 9?	4
18.	Look at circle A on your sheet. It has been cut into halves. Color the half on the right-hand side. To which numeral does the minute hand of an analog clock point at half past 9?	6
	Show how the minute hand has swept over half of the clock face. Hence "half past."	
19.	Look at circle B on your sheet. It has been cut into 4. Each part is called "a quarter." Color the quarter on the top left side.	teacher
20.	Count by fives to find how many minutes in a quarter of an hour.	15 min
	Show how the minute hand has swept over three quarters of the clock face. Hence "a quarter to."	

Additional Material Needed

Something to measure child's height, room thermometer

1. _____ 6. _____ 11. _____ 16. _____

2. _____ 7. _____ 12. _____ 17. _____

3. _____ 8. _____ 13. _____ 18. _____

4. _____ 9. _____ 14. _____ 19. **on diagram**

5. _____ 10. _____ 15. _____ 20. _____

1–8

9–11

square pyramid

sphere

cube

15–16

* "peri" means "around"

** "metron" means "measure"

*** "perimeter" means "distance around"

```
        3 units                          8 units
2 units  [ A ]  2 units        3 units  [  B  ]  3 units
        3 units                          8 units
```

17–20

Fives pattern   5 10 15 20 25 30 35 40 45 50 55 60

analog clock

A   B

Activity

1. Copy the information marked with stars for questions 15 and 16.

* " ___ ___ ___ " ___ ___ ___ ___ ___   " ___ ___ ___ ___ ___ ___ "

** " ___ ___ ___ ___ " ___ ___ ___ ___   " ___ ___ ___ ___ ___ ___ ___ "

*** " ___ ___ ___ ___ ___ ___ ___ ___ ___ " ___ ___ ___ ___ ___ ___

" ___ ___ ___ ___ ___ ___ ___ ___ " ___ ___ ___ ___ ___ ___

BLAST 13

Number	Question and Discussion	Answer
1.	Within 10 degrees Celsius, estimate the temperature in the classroom right now. Write the "degrees Celsius" abbreviation as part of your answer.	teacher
2.	Close your eyes and count to estimate the number of seconds between when I say "start" and "stop." Your answer should end in 0 or 5.	teacher
	Allow the stopwatch to run for 65 seconds.	

(i) Questions 3 to 5 relate to the 2-D (or plane) shapes on your sheet. Notice the bugs in each "corner" (or angle) of the square.

3.	Draw a bug in each corner (or angle) of the pentagon. Write the number of bugs you draw on answer line 3.	5
4.	Draw a bug in each corner (or angle) of the octagon. Write the number of bugs you draw on answer line 4.	8
5.	Draw a bug in each corner (or angle) of the hexagon. Write the number of bugs you draw on answer line 5.	6
	Choose a child from the class.	
6.	Estimate this person's height.	teacher
7.	Estimate the height of the bookshelf.	teacher
8.	How many socks make up 8 "pairs"?	16
9.	Henry had 9 marbles in his right hand and 7 in his left hand. "Count forward" from 7 to find out how many more he has in his right hand than his left hand.	2
	When subtracting (or finding the difference between) numbers that are close to each other, it is often quickest to "count forward" from the smaller number.	

(i) Use the grid to answer questions 10 to 19.

10.	Draw the shape in grid space (A, 4).	star
11.	Draw the shape in grid space (C, 1).	sad face
12.	Draw the shape in grid space (D, 2).	happy face
13.	Draw the shape in grid space (B, 3).	circle
14.	Draw the shape in grid space (A, 1).	cloud

Notice that when I was calling grid positions I called the "across" (horizontal) reference first and then the "up and down" (vertical) reference. Grid references are always called in this order, across first, then up and down.

(i) Make sure when you answer the following questions that you write the "across" reference first and then the "up and down" reference.

15.	Which grid space shows a picture of a square?	D4
16.	Which grid space shows a picture of a triangle?	C2
17.	Which grid space shows a picture of a question mark?	A2
18.	Which grid space shows a picture of an exclamation mark?	B1
19.	Which grid space is blank?	B2
20.	Estimate the perimeter of a window in the classroom.	teacher

Additional Material Needed

Room thermometer, stopwatch, something to measure child's height, meter stick or tape measure for question 20

Activity Answers

1. teacher   2.   (a) 2   (b) 4   (c) 1   (d) 3   (e) 3   (f) 3

1. _____	6. _____	11. _____	16. _____
2. _____	7. _____	12. _____	17. _____
3. _____	8. _____	13. _____	18. _____
4. _____	9. _____	14. _____	19. _____
5. _____	10. _____	15. _____	20. _____

3–5

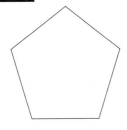 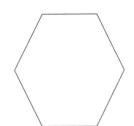 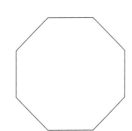 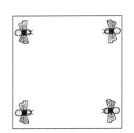

pentagon   hexagon   octagon   square

8

Two things make a pair.

10–19

	A	B	C	D
4	☆	,	✔	▢
3		○		X
2	?		△	☺
1		!	☹	

Activity

1. Draw the minute hand on these analog clocks to show the times written underneath.

9:00   9:05   9:10   9:15   9:20   9:25   9:30

2. "Count forward" to do these subtraction problems.

(a) $11 - 9 =$ _____

(b) $12 - 8 =$ _____

(c) $11 - 10 =$ _____

(d) $10 - 7 =$ _____

(e) $14 - 11 =$ _____

(f) $13 - 10 =$ _____

BLAST 14

Number	Question and Discussion	Answer
ⓘ	Refer to the pictures of rooms to answer questions 1 to 3. Colin has put square tiles on the floor of the 3 rooms shown.	
1.	How many tiles were needed in the bedroom?	9
2.	How many tiles were needed to cover the playroom floor?	16
3.	How many were needed to cover the floor of the dining room?	12
4.	Which orange has been cut in "half"?	A
ⓘ	Imagine that you are a bird flying over some solid shapes that the children forgot to pack away. Use the letters (A, B, C, or D) to answer the next 4 questions.	
5.	Which shape is a cone?	A
6.	Which shape is a cube?	B
7.	Which shape is a cylinder?	D
8.	Which shape is a square pyramid?	C
ⓘ	Look at the pictures of corners (or angles) on your sheet. Run your finger over corner (angle) ABC. Now run your finger over corner (angle) XYZ.	
9.	Which corner would hurt most if you stepped on it with bare feet?	XYZ

Corners are also called "angles" in mathematics. A "triangle" has "three (tri) angles."

ⓘ	Questions 10 to 15 relate to the letters and numbers on your sheet. When you have worked out the answer, write the letter that matches it on the answer line.	
10.	Mark bought 4 pairs of socks. How many socks is this altogether? Write the letter that matches your answer.	A
11.	Jody planted 3 rows of cabbages. Each row has 4 cabbages in it. How many cabbages is this altogether? Write the letter that matches your answer.	C
12.	Joshua had 2 plums at recess every school day last week. How many plums is this altogether? Write the letter that matches your answer.	U
13.	Hayley's 3 hens each had 3 chicks. How many chicks is this altogether? Write the letter that matches your answer.	T
14.	Anne's mother has 2 newspapers delivered to her home daily. How many newspapers is this altogether in week? Write the letter that matches your answer.	E
15.	If you were correct, the last 5 answers spell another word for a sharp corner or angle. Write the word by writing the letters in order from answers 10 to 14.	ACUTE

Choose a child from the class.

16.	Estimate this person's height within 20 cm.	teacher
17.	Estimate the width of the doorway.	teacher
18.	Within 10 degrees Celsius, estimate the temperature in the classroom right now. Write the "degrees Celsius" abbreviation as part of your answer.	teacher
19.	Which temperature on your sheet do you think is closest to the temperature in your refrigerator? Write the "degrees Celsius" abbreviation as part of your answer.	4°C
20.	Which temperature on your sheet do you think is closest to the temperature on a hot summer day? Write the "degrees Celsius" abbreviation as part of your answer.	38°C

Additional Material Needed

Something to measure child's height, room thermometer

Activity Answers

1. (a) vertical (b) oblique (c) horizontal

1. _____	6. _____	11. _____	16. _____
2. _____	7. _____	12. _____	17. _____
3. _____	8. _____	13. _____	18. _____
4. _____	9. _____	14. _____	19. _____
5. _____	10. _____	15. _____	20. _____

1–3   bedroom   dining room   playroom

4   A   B   C

5–8   A   B   C   D

9   B   A   C   Y   X   Z

10–15   8=A 9=T 10=U 11=S 12=C 14=E

19–20   0°C   4°C   38°C

Activity

1. Match the word with its line. Copy the word on the lines provided.

        horizontal   vertical   oblique

(a) _____

(b) _____

(c) _____   (a)   (b)   (c)

BLAST 15

Number	Question and Discussion	Answer
(i)	Imagine that you are a bird flying over some solid shapes that the children in your class forgot to pack away. Use the letters to answer the first 4 questions.	
1.	Which picture looks like a sphere when looked at from above?	D
2.	Which picture looks like a triangular pyramid when looked at from above?	E
3.	Which picture looks like a rectangular prism when looked at from above?	A
4.	Which picture looks like a triangular prism when looked at from above?	B
(i)	Questions 5–13 relate to the letters and numbers on your sheet. When you have worked out the answer, write the letter that matches it on your answer lines.	
5.	How many sides do 3 triangles have altogether? Write the letter that matches your answer.	R
6.	How many shoes are needed for 7 children? Write the letter that matches your answer.	E
7.	Fido has 8 bones and Rover has 7. If they combined them, how many bones would they have? Write the letter that matches your answer.	D
8.	What is the "difference" between the number of bones Fido has and the number Rover has? Write the letter that matches your answer.	N
9.	Look at the picture of the spider on your sheet. If spiders wore socks, how many socks would two spiders need? Write the letter that matches your answer.	I
10.	Robbie Rocker has 2 rings on each finger and the thumb of his right hand. How many rings is this altogether? Write the letter that matches your answer.	L
11.	Amanda collects shells. She has 7 in her collection. One day she goes to the beach and collects 5 more. How many does she have altogether? Write the letter that matches your answer.	Y
12.	There are 10 pencils on Kurt's table. Matthew borrows 4. How many are still on Kurt's table? Write the letter that matches your answer.	C
13.	Read the letters backwards from answers 12 to 5. They spell the name of a solid shape. Write the word on answer line 13.	CYLINDER
(i)	Questions 14–18 are about the grid on your sheet. Listen carefully to the instructions given and follow carefully with your finger. Draw the shape that you finish on for your answer. Always begin at the starting point for each new question.	
14.	Move 3 right, then 1 up. Draw the shape you finish on.	star
15.	Move 2 right, then 2 up. Draw the shape you finish on.	circle
16.	Move 5 right, then 3 up, then 1 left. Draw the shape you finish on.	square
17.	Move 2 right, then 1 up, then 2 right, then 1 down. Draw the shape you finish on.	apple
18.	Draw the shape already in the box if the apple moved 1 up, then 1 right.	checkmark
	Choose a child from the class.	
19.	Estimate this person's height.	teacher
20.	Estimate the length of your desk.	teacher

Additional Material Needed

Something to measure a child's height

Activity Answers

1. (a) green   (b) purple   (c) 5   (d) 6   (e) 25

1. _____ 6. _____ 11. _____ 16. _____

2. _____ 7. _____ 12. _____ 17. _____

3. _____ 8. _____ 13. _____ 18. _____

4. _____ 9. _____ 14. _____ 19. _____

5. _____ 10. _____ 15. _____ 20. _____

1-4

A   B   C   D   E   F

5-13

1=N   4=S   5=B   6=C   9=R   10=L   12=Y   14=E   15=D   16=I   17=X   20=W

14-18

				?
△			□	
	○			
		☆		✔
Start here			🍎	

Activity

1. Your class did a survey and used the tally method to record results. The survey asked children to tell what their favorite color was. Use the information shown to answer the questions.

red   ‖‖‖‖

yellow   ‖‖‖

blue   ‖‖‖‖ ‖

green   ‖‖‖‖ ‖‖‖‖

purple   ‖

(a) Which color was most popular? _____

(b) Which color was least popular? _____

(c) How many children liked red the best? _____

(d) How many children liked blue the best? _____

(e) How many children took part in this survey altogether? _____

History: The word "tally" comes from an old French word meaning "twig" or "stick." Tallies were originally kept by cutting notches on a stick.

BLAST 16

Number	Question and Discussion	Answer

i To answer questions 1 to 6, refer to the drawings representing 3-D, or solid, things. Write the name of the things made from the 3-D shapes given.

1. Which thing is made up of a square pyramid and a cube? — house

2. Which thing is made up of a rectangular prism and 4 cylinders? — bus

3. Which thing is made up of a cone and a cylinder? — pencil

4. Which thing is made up of a sphere and a cone? — wizard

5. Which thing is made up of a sphere and a cylinder? — candy apple

6. Which thing is made up of a rectangular prism and 2 cylinders? — factory

The words on your sheet are used to describe temperature. A thermometer is used to measure temperature.

i Use the letters above the thermometers to answer the next 4 questions. All temperatures are in degrees Celsius.

7. Which thermometer shows the temperature of boiling water? — W

8. Which thermometer shows the temperature of an ice cube? — M

9. Which thermometer shows the temperature on a hot summer day? — A

10. Which thermometer shows the temperature on a pleasant spring day? — R

11. Put the pictures in order from hottest to coldest. Use the letters and you will write a word that has something to do with temperature. — warm

Flip a coin (or choose a child to flip a coin) 10 times. Call the results aloud progressively; e.g., "heads," "tails" and so on.

12-13 Tally the results for "heads" on answer line 12 and "tails" on answer line 13. — teacher

i Questions 14 to 17 refer to the 4 letters shown on your sheet. Trace over the outline of the flipped letters "L," "J," "G" and "R."

14. Draw the letter "L" as it looks flipped over on answer line 14. — ⌐

15. Draw the letter "J" as it looks flipped over on answer line 15. — ℓ

16. Draw the letter "G" as it looks flipped over on answer line 16. — ಧ

17. Draw the letter "R" as it looks flipped over on answer line 17. — Я

18. Try drawing what the capital letter B would look like if it was flipped. — ଶ

Choose a child from the class.

19. Estimate this person's height within 20 cm. — teacher

20. Estimate the distance from the door to the teacher's desk in the classroom. — teacher

Additional Material Needed

Something to measure child's height, coin

BLAST 16 WORKSHEET

A BLAST OF MATH

1. _____   6. _____   11. _____   16. _____
2. _____   7. _____   12. **Heads** _____   17. _____
3. _____   8. _____   13. **Tails** _____   18. _____
4. _____   9. _____   14. _____   19. _____
5. _____   10. _____   15. _____   20. _____

1–6

pencil   bus   factory   house   wizard   candy apple

7–10

A thermometer is used to measure temperature.

M   R   A   W

| boiling |
| freezing |
| hot |
| pleasant |

14–17

L J G R

11

R   A   M   W

Activity

Number pictures

1. Bernard Butterfly is going for a walk among the flowers in Numberland. Draw your own picture made up entirely of numerals.

BLAST 17

Number	Question and Discussion	Answer
	The first 5 questions are about the clocks on your sheet. Use the letters to answer the questions.	
1.	Clock 1 shows the time as 5 minutes past 7. Which clock shows the time 5 minutes to 7?	W
2.	Clock 2 shows the time as 10 minutes past 7. Which clock shows the time 10 minutes to 7?	A
3.	Clock 3 shows the time as 15 minutes past 7. Which clock shows the time 15 minutes to 7?	T
4.	Clock 4 shows the time as 20 minutes past 7. Which clock shows the time 20 minutes to 7?	C
5.	Clock 5 shows the time as 25 minutes past 7. Which clock shows the time 25 minutes to 7?	H

Answers spell "watch."

	Look at the partly shaded rectangle on your sheet. Refer to it when answering questions 6 to 10.	
6.	How many equal-sized parts is the rectangle broken into?	2
7.	How many parts are shaded?	1
8.	What fraction of the shape is shaded?	$\frac{1}{2}$
9.	How many parts are unshaded?	1
10.	What fraction of the shape is unshaded?	$\frac{1}{2}$

The bottom number in a fraction is the number of equal-size-parts a shape has been broken into.

The top number in a fraction is the number of those parts we are considering.

	Questions 11 to 17 relate to the letters and lines on your sheet.	
11.	Draw what you would see if you "turned" capital "A" to the right until it was resting on the line.	⊣A (rotated A)
12.	Draw what you would see if you "turned" capital "E" to the right until it was resting on the line.	(rotated E)
13.	Draw what you would see if you "turned" capital "K" to the right until it was resting on the line.	(rotated K)
14.	Draw what you would see if you "turned" capital "A" to the left until it was resting on the line.	(rotated A)
15.	Draw what you would see if you "turned" capital "E" to the left until it was resting on the line.	(rotated E)
16.	Draw what you would see if you "turned" capital "K" to the left until it was resting on the line.	(rotated K)
17.	Which letter looks the same whether you turn it to the right or left?	H

Pictures W, X, Y and Z show shapes A, B, C and D drawn from above.

18.	Which one matches A?	W
19.	Which one matches B?	Y
20.	Which one matches C?	Z

Activity Answers

1.	(a) B	(b) 3	(c) 5
2.	(a) A	(b) 4	(c) 6
3.	(a) D	(b) 5	(c) 7
4.	(a) C	(b) 6	(c) 8

1. _____	6. _____	11. _____	16. _____
2. _____	7. _____	12. _____	17. _____
3. _____	8. _____	13. _____	18. _____
4. _____	9. _____	14. _____	19. _____
5. _____	10. _____	15. _____	20. _____

1–5

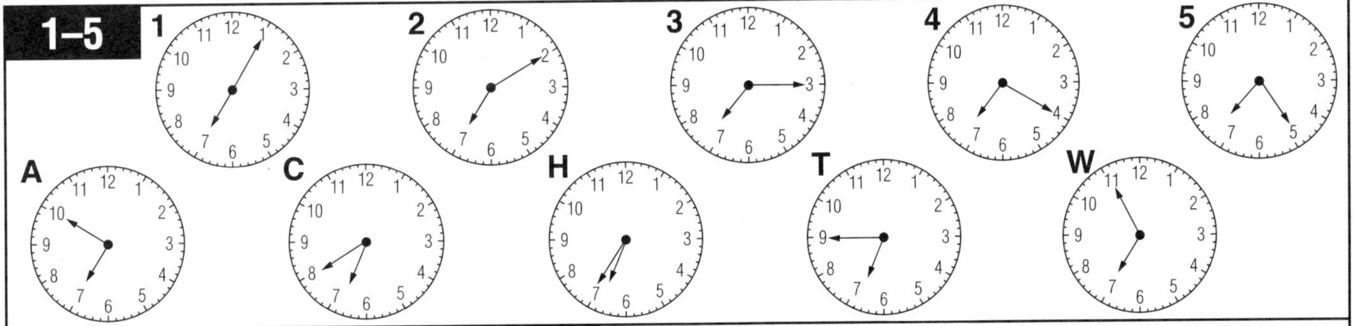

1 2 3 4 5

A C H T W

6–10

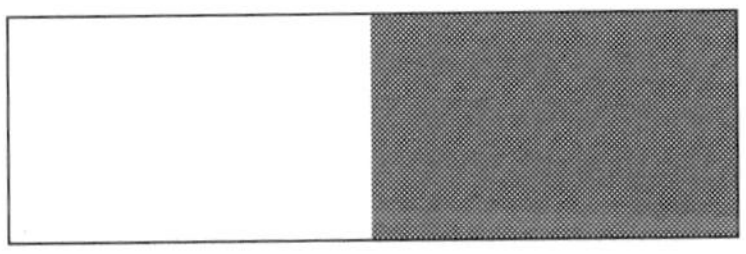

11–17

_____ A _____   _____ E _____

_____ K _____   _____ H _____

18–20

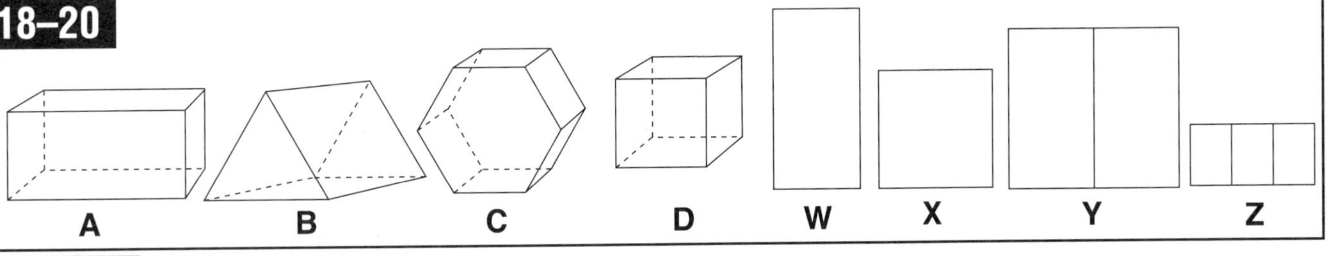

A B C D W X Y Z

Activity

Prisms

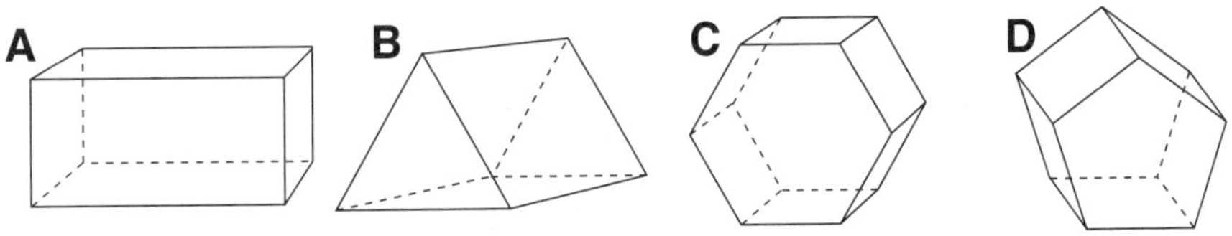

A B C D

1. (a) Which shape is a triangular prism? _____

(b) How many sides does a triangle have? _____

(c) How many faces does a triangular prism have? _____

2. (a) Which shape is a rectangular prism? _____

(b) How many sides does a rectangle have? _____

(c) How many faces does a rectangular prism have? _____

3. (a) Which shape is a pentagonal prism? _____

(b) How many sides does a pentagon have? _____

(c) How many faces does a pentagonal prism have? _____

4. (a) Which shape is a hexagonal prism?

_____

(b) How many sides does a hexagon have?

_____

(c) How many faces does a hexagonal prism have?

_____

BLAST 18

Number	Question and Discussion	Answer

 Look at the numbers on answer lines 1 to 6. We are going to tally our results as we roll a die. First, in the space marked "est." on answer line 7, write your estimate for the number of throws it will take before every number appears at least once.

Choose a child or some children to roll a die and call results aloud to the class.

Write tally marks as each number is called. We will continue tallying until each number has been called at least once.   teacher

7. Write the actual number of throws it took for every number to come up in the space marked "act."   teacher

8. Add 2 curved lines to the shape on answer line 8 to turn it into a picture of a common 3-D shape.

9. Write the smallest 3-digit numeral you can using the digits 8, 3 and 5.   358

10. Write the largest 3-digit numeral you can using the same numerals.   853

 To answer the next 5 questions, refer to the picture of the partly shaded rectangle on your sheet.

11. How many equal-sized parts is the rectangle cut into?   4

12. How many parts are shaded?   1

13. What fraction is shaded? $\frac{1}{4}$

14. How many parts are not shaded?   3

15. What fraction is not shaded? $\frac{3}{4}$

 The picture on your sheet represents a square pyramid. The letters stand for the parts of the pyramid that are pointed to. The words next to the shape are the names of these parts. Match the letter to its correct name to answer the next 2 questions.

16. What part of the pyramid is arrow "B" pointing to?   base

17. What part of the pyramid is arrow "A" pointing to?   apex

 Match the times shown on the digital and analog clocks to answer questions 18 to 20.

18. Which digital clock is showing the same time as analog clock X?   B

19. Which digital clock is showing the same time as analog clock Z?   C

20. Which analog clock is showing the same time as digital clock A?   Y

Additional Material Needed

Die

Activity Answers

1. (a) 30   (b) 31   (c) February   (d) 29   (e) 31

2. cube – B; cylinder – D; square pyramid – E; rectangular prism – C; triangular pyramid – A

---

1. ___1s___	6. ___6s___	11. _____	16. _____
2. ___2s___	7. ___est.___ ___act.___	12. _____	17. _____
3. ___3s___	8. _____	13. _____	18. _____
4. ___4s___	9. _____	14. _____	19. _____
5. ___5s___	10. _____	15. _____	20. _____

11–15

16–17

base
apex

18–20

analog   digital

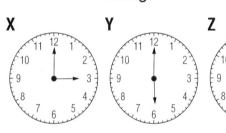

X   Y   Z

A **6:00**

B **3:00**

C **8:00**

Activity

1. Read the rhyme, then answer the questions.

> *Thirty days have September*
> *April, June and November*
> *All the rest have thirty-one*
> *Excepting February alone*
> *Which has twenty-eight days clear*
> *And twenty-nine in each leap year*

(a) How many days in June? _____

(b) How many days in December? _____

(c) Which is the shortest month? _____

(d) How many days in February in a leap year? _____

(e) How many days in August? _____

2. Match the "nets" with their names.

cube   cylinder   square pyramid   rectangular prism   triangular pyramid

A   B   C   D   E

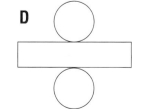
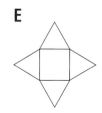

BLAST 19

Number	Question and Discussion	Answer
	Match the 3 number sentences on your sheet with the following stories.	
1.	There were 8 birds in a tree and 3 flew away. Write the number sentence that matches this story.	$8 - 3 = 5$
2.	Jake collects baseball cards. He had 8 and on his birthday was given 3 more. Write the number sentence that matches this story.	$8 + 3 = 11$
3.	There are 8 trees in the park next to my home. Each tree has 3 birds nesting in it. Write the number sentence that matches this story.	$8 \times 3 = 24$
	Match the digital and analog clocks in the next 3 questions.	
4.	Which analog clock matches digital clock X?	A
5.	Which analog clock matches digital clock Z?	C
6.	Which digital clock matches analog clock B?	Y
	The next 5 questions are about the picture showing a group of marbles on your sheet.	
7.	How many marbles in this group altogether?	2
8.	How many of the marbles are colored?	1
9.	What fraction of the group of marbles is colored?	$\frac{1}{2}$
	You can think of this as "1 out of 2."	
10.	How many marbles in the group are clear?	1
11.	What fraction of the group of marbles is clear?	$\frac{1}{2}$
	You can think of this as "1 out of 2."	
	Questions 12 to 18 relate to the letters and numbers on your sheet. When you have worked out the answer, write the letter that matches it. Use the hundreds chart if you are unsure about working the answers out in your head.	
12.	7 plus 6. Write the letter that matches your answer.	P
13.	Add 6 to 17. Write the letter that matches your answer.	R
14.	What is the sum of 26 and 7? Write the letter that matches your answer.	O
15.	What is the total of 37 and 6? Write the letter that matches your answer.	D
16.	Add 6 to 47. Write the letter that matches your answer.	U
17.	How many is 6 added to 57? Write the letter that matches your answer.	C
18.	What number is 6 more than 67? Write the letter that matches your answer.	T
	The answers spell the word "product." This is another "math word." In mathematics the "product" is the answer we get when we "multiply."	
19.	Close your eyes and estimate, to the nearest five seconds, the number of seconds between when I say "start" and "stop." Your answer should end in "0" or "5."	teacher
	Allow the stopwatch to run for 80 seconds.	
20.	Estimate the temperature in the classroom right now. Write the "degrees Celsius" abbreviation as part of your answer.	teacher

Additional Material Needed

Stopwatch, room thermometer

Activity Answers

1. product
2. (a) 5   (b) 2   (c) $\frac{2}{5}$ (d) 3   (e) $\frac{3}{5}$ (f) teacher

1. _____	6. _____	11. _____	16. _____
2. _____	7. _____	12. _____	17. _____
3. _____	8. _____	13. _____	18. _____
4. _____	9. _____	14. _____	19. _____
5. _____	10. _____	15. _____	20. _____

1–3    8+3=11   8−3=5   8x3=24

4–6   analog   digital

A   B   C   X **6:00**

Y **3:00**

Z **8:00**

Hundreds Chart

1	2	3	4	5	6	7	8	9	10
11	12	13	14	15	16	17	18	19	20
21	22	23	24	25	26	27	28	29	30
31	32	33	34	35	36	37	38	39	40
41	42	43	44	45	46	47	48	49	50
51	52	53	54	55	56	57	58	59	60
61	62	63	64	65	66	67	68	69	70
71	72	73	74	75	76	77	78	79	80
81	82	83	84	85	86	87	88	89	90
91	92	93	94	95	96	97	98	99	100

7–11

12–18

A=83   B=93   C=63   D=43   O=33

P=13   R=23   T=73   U=53

Activity

1. Complete the sentence by writing the letters from answers 12 to 18 in order.

    The answer we get when we multiply is called the _____.

2. Fractions (whole things in a group)

   (a)   How many cars altogether? _____

   (b)   How many black cars? _____

   (c)   What fraction of the group of cars is black (how many out of how many)? _____

   (d)   How many white cars? _____

   (e)   What fraction of the group of cars is white (how many out of how many)? _____

   (f)   Color $^3/_5$ of the cars red.

BLAST 20

Number	Question and Discussion	Answer
(i)	Questions 1–3 refer to the pictures of analog clocks on your sheet.	
1.	Which clock shows the time when many children would be getting ready to go to school?	A
2.	Which clock shows the time when many children would be having lunch?	C
3.	Which clock shows the time when many teachers would be asking children to pack up and get ready to go home?	B
(i)	The next 5 questions are about the picture showing a group of marbles on your sheet.	
4.	How many marbles are in this group altogether?	3
5.	How many marbles are colored?	1
6.	What fraction of the group of marbles is colored?	$^1/_3$
7.	How many marbles in the group are clear?	2
8.	What fraction of the group of marbles is clear?	$^2/_3$
(i)	Use the abbreviations for the months to answer the next 4 questions.	
9.	Which is the first month of the year with only 30 days in it?	Apr.
10.	Which is the last month with only 30 days in it?	Nov.
11.	List the months of fall.	Sept., Oct., Nov.
12.	Which has more days, September or January?	Jan.
(i)	Look at the picture representing stacked cubes on your sheet.	
13.	How many boxes must be added to the stack to make it a triangle shape?	3
14.	If you were going to add another row to the bottom, how many boxes would be in it?	5
(i)	The remaining questions are about the balance scale on your sheet. Each ball stands for 1 kilogram weight.	
15.	How many 1-kilogram weights must be added to Y so that it balances with X?	3
16.	How many 1-kilogram weights could you take away from X to make it balance with Y?	3
17.	If you add 3 weights to X, how many would you have to add to Y to make the arms balance?	6
18.	If you add 5 weights to Y, how many would you have to add to X so the arms balance?	2
19.	Without changing the number of weights, which direction could you move the bucket at X to make the arms balance? Draw a direction arrow like the one on your sheet.	→
20.	Without changing the number of weights, which direction could you move the bucket at Y to make the arms balance? Draw a direction arrow like the one on your sheet.	→

Activity Answers

1. (a) 25¢, 25¢, 25¢   (b) 50¢, 10¢, 5¢   (c) 50¢, 25¢, 25¢   (d) $1, 25¢, 5¢
   (e) $1, 50¢, 25¢   (f) $1, 50¢, 50¢

1. _____   6. _____   11. _____   16. _____

2. _____   7. _____   12. _____   17. _____

3. _____   8. _____   13. _____   18. _____

4. _____   9. _____   14. _____   19. _____

5. _____   10. _____   15. _____   20. _____

1–3

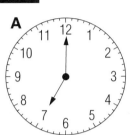 **A**   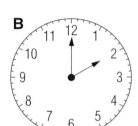 **B**   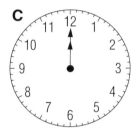 **C**

4–8

9–12

Thirty days have September

April, June and November

All the rest have thirty-one

Excepting February alone

Which has twenty-eight days clear

And twenty-nine in each leap year

Abbreviations

Jan.	Feb.	Mar.	Apr.
May	Jun.	Jul.	Aug.
Sept.	Oct.	Nov.	Dec.

13–14

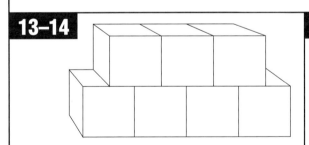

15–20

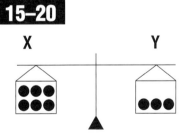
X   Y

Direction arrows

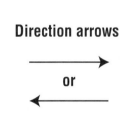

or

Activity

Our coins are 1¢, 5¢, 10¢, 25¢, 50¢ and $1.

1. Write 3 coins you could use to make each amount.

    (a)   75¢ = 25¢, 25¢, 25¢,

    (b)   65¢ = _____, _____, _____

    (c) $1.00 = _____, _____, _____

    (d) $1.30 = _____, _____, _____

    (e) $1.75 = _____, _____, _____

    (f) $2.00 = _____, _____, _____

BLAST 21

Number	Question and Discussion	Answer
	Use one of the answers written on your sheet to answer the first 2 questions.	
1.	Which direction did the water in the bathtub go when Clarence stepped into it?	up
2.	Which direction did the water in the pot go when Maddie lifted her boiled egg out?	down
	The next 3 questions are about what things look like when looked at from above.	
3.	Which picture shows a car?	B
4.	Which picture shows a table?	A
5.	Which picture shows a boy?	C
6.	Corinne has 6 goldfish. She buys 3 more. How many does she have now?	9
7.	Max has 60 coins. His dad gives him 30 more for his birthday. How many does he have now?	90
8.	There are 600 fleas on Rover and 300 on Fido. How many fleas are on the dogs altogether?	900
	Note the link: 6 + 3 = 9; 60 + 30 = 90; 600 + 300 = 900.	
9.	Look at the groups of marbles on your sheet. Which group could be shared equally between 2 friends?	B
	Division is well illustrated by sharing.	
	Look at the list of our coins. You may use the same coin more than once when answering the next 3 questions.	
10.	Which 3 coins could be used to make up 75¢?	25¢, 25¢, 25¢
11.	Which 3 coins could be used to make up 55¢?	25¢, 25¢, 5¢
12.	Which 3 coins could be used to make up 80¢?	50¢, 25¢, 5¢
	Omar had sandwiches for lunch last week. To keep him guessing, his mother cut them a different way each day. You can see on your sheet how she cut them. Use the abbreviations to answer the next 5 questions. By the way, Omar always eats all of his lunch. Not a single crumb is left behind.	
13.	On which day did he eat 4 triangular prisms?	Thurs.
14.	On which day did he eat 2 rectangular prisms?	Tues.
15.	On which day did he eat 4 square prisms?	Fri.
16.	On which day did he eat 1 square prism?	Mon.
17.	On which day did he eat 2 triangular prisms?	Wed.
	Write "G" for "good value" or "P" for "poor value" for the items mentioned in the next 3 questions.	
18.	A piece of bubble gum for $5.00.	P
19.	A carton of chocolate milk for 20¢.	G
20.	A dozen rotten eggs for 1¢.	P

A BLAST OF MATH - BOOK 1   World Teachers Press®

1. _____   6. _____   11. _____   16. _____

2. _____   7. _____   12. _____   17. _____

3. _____   8. _____   13. _____   18. _____

4. _____   9. _____   14. _____   19. _____

5. _____   10. _____   15. _____   20. _____

1–2

stayed the same   down   up

3–5

A   B   C

9

A = ◯ ◯ ◯

B = ◯ ◯ ◯ ◯

13–17

Mon.   Tues.

Wed.   Thurs.   Fri.

10–12

5¢   10¢   25¢   50¢ $1

18–20

G = good value

P = poor value

Activity

1. Color the blobs using different colors, then go over the matching lines using the same color.

    For example—color the "horizontal" blob red, then go over the horizontal line in red.

    horizontal ⬚   vertical ⬚   oblique ⬚ zigzag ⬚

    dotted ⬚   wavy ⬚   curved ⬚

BLAST 22

Number	Question and Discussion	Answer
	To answer the first 3 questions, refer to the road sign or map.	
1.	How far is it from the road sign to Chum?	1 km
2.	How far is it from Tum to Plum?	2 km
3.	How far from Tum to Fo Fum?	7 km
	Write the letter to match the lines with their names for questions 4-7.	
4.	Which letter names the picture of one oblique line?	B
5.	Which letter names the picture of one vertical line?	A
6.	Which letter names the picture of parallel lines?	E
7.	Which letter names the picture of one horizontal line?	C
8.	Alicia has 3 comic books. She buys 4 more. How many does she have now?	7
9.	The teacher has graded 30 tests. There are still 40 to grade. How many tests must she grade altogether?	70
10.	Our school concert ran for 2 nights. On the first night 300 people attended. On the second, 400 attended. How many attended over the 2 nights?	700
11.	Snow White bought each of the seven dwarfs a pair of gloves. How many gloves is this altogether?	14
12.	What is the smallest coin in our money (in terms of size, not value)?	dime
	Write "G" for "good value" or "P" for "poor value" to answer questions 13 to 15.	
13.	A box of 24 colored pencils for $1.00.	G
14.	A chocolate bar for $20.00.	P
15.	A $1.00 coin from Australia with the year 1834 on it for $5.00.	G

As collector's items, some things have a much greater value than their face value. To know if something is a good buy you sometimes need to find out from an expert or do your own research.

	Match the instrument with what it measures in the next 3 questions. First of all we will look at each word and say it. Write the words and answers.	
16.	Which instrument measures mass (weight)?	scale
17.	Which instrument measures temperature?	thermometer
18.	Which instrument measures length?	ruler
19.	Estimate the temperature in the classroom right now. Write the "degrees Celsius" abbreviation as part of your answer.	teacher
20.	Estimate the distance from one point to another in the classroom.	teacher

Additional Material Needed

Room thermometer

Activity Answers

1.	(a) 4 x 2 = 8	(b) 2 x 3 = 6	(c) 3 x 4 = 12	(d) 2 x 5 = 10	(e) 3 x 5 = 15	
2.	(a) 256	(b) 439	(c) 568	(d) 184	(e) 365	(f) 917
3.	365					

1. _____ 6. _____ 11. _____ 16. _____

2. _____ 7. _____ 12. _____ 17. _____

3. _____ 8. _____ 13. _____ 18. _____

4. _____ 9. _____ 14. _____ 19. _____

5. _____ 10. _____ 15. _____ 20. _____

1–3

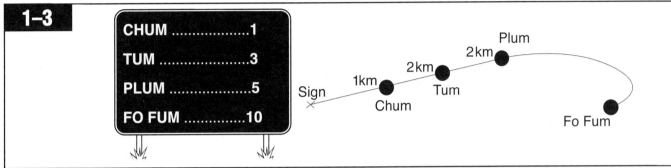

CHUM 1
TUM 3
PLUM 5
FO FUM 10

4–7

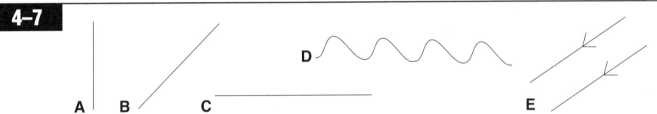

A   B   C   D   E

13–15

G = good value

P = poor value

16–18

ruler	thermometer	analog clock	scale

Activity

1. Write the "multiplication" number sentences for the groups below.

(a)   xx xx xx xx   Number sentence = __4__ x __2__ = __8__

(b)   ooo ooo   Number sentence = _____ x _____ = _____

(c)   VVVV VVVV VVVV   Number sentence = _____ x _____ = _____

(d)   XXXXX XXXXX   Number sentence = _____ x _____ = _____

(e)   ***** ***** *****   Number sentence = _____ x _____ = _____

2. Write the numbers made by the groups of ones, tens and hundreds.

(a)   200 + 50 + 6 = __256__

(b)   400 + 30 + 9 = _____

(c)   500 + 60 + 8 = _____

(d)   100 + 80 + 4 = _____

(e)   300 + 60 + 5 = _____

(f)   900 + 10 + 7 = _____

3. Which of these numbers is the number of days in a year? _____

BLAST 23

Number	Question and Discussion	Answer
1.	A chimp has 9 bananas. He eats 6. How many remain uneaten?	3
2.	There are 90 ants marching in a line. Sixty break away from the line and go over to where the family is having a picnic. How many are still in the line?	30
3.	Nadya has 900 stamps. She sells 600 to a stamp dealer. How many does she have left?	300
ⓘ	Questions 4 and 5 are about things used in measuring. Choose from the names on the sheet to write your answer.	
	Read the words with the class.	
4.	Which would you use to measure a volume of liquid?	measuring cup
5.	Which would you use to measure a person's waist?	tape measure
ⓘ	Look at the letters on your sheet. Axes of symmetry have been drawn on them. Draw axes of symmetry on the letters on answer lines 6 to 9.	
6.		– **C** –
7.		– **D** –
8.		– **H** –
9.		**M**
ⓘ	The next 5 questions relate to the picture of a group of marbles on your sheet. You may want to trace very lightly on your sheet with a pencil or your finger to do the groupings that follow. Do them in your mind if you can.	
10.	If the marbles were put into bags with 5 marbles in each, how many bags would be needed?	2
11.	When you do this example you will have a remainder. If the marbles were put into bags with 3 marbles in each, how many bags would be needed?	3
12.	How many marbles would be left over?	1
13.	When you do this example you will have a remainder. If the marbles were put into bags with 4 marbles in each, how many bags would be needed?	2
14.	How many marbles would be left over?	2
ⓘ	Choose from the temperatures on your answer sheet to do questions 15 to 17. Include the abbreviation for "degrees Celsius" in your answer.	
15.	Which temperature would it be on a hot summer's day?	35°C
16.	Which temperature would an ice cube have?	0°C
17.	Which temperature would be most likely in your refrigerator (not the freezer)?	4°C
18.	Estimate the temperature in the classroom right now. Write the "degrees Celsius" abbreviation as part of your answer.	teacher
19.	Close your eyes and estimate, to the nearest five seconds, the number of seconds between when I say "start" and "stop." Your answer should end in 0 or 5.	teacher
	Allow the stopwatch to run for 75 seconds.	
20.	Estimate the distance from one point to another in the classroom.	teacher

Additional Material Needed

Room thermometer, stopwatch

1. _____	6. ___C___	11. _____	16. _____
2. _____	7. ___D___	12. _____	17. _____
3. _____	8. ___H___	13. _____	18. _____
4. _____	9. ___M___	14. _____	19. _____
5. _____	10. _____	15. _____	20. _____

4–5

measuring cup   thermometer   tape measure   ruler

6–9

Examples

- B -

O

10–14

15–17

0°C   100°C   35°C   4°C

Activity

1. Draw the other half of each "symmetrical" shape.

  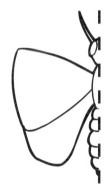

2. **Measuring time:**

People first knew about time of day by the position of the sun in the sky.

In an hourglass, it took the sand one hour to flow from the top to the bottom. Then it had to be turned over.

The candle clock burns down at the rate of one mark per hour.

The big clock is called a grandfather clock. The smaller one is called a grandmother clock.

A visually impaired person can tell the time on a watch by feeling the hands or by listening to a "talking" watch.

BLAST 24

Number	Question and Discussion	Answer
(i)	The first 3 questions relate to the 2-D shapes on the sheet. Listen to the descriptions, then match the shape with its name.	
1.	A trapezoid has 4 sides. Only 2 of the sides are parallel. Which shape is a trapezoid?	B
2.	A parallelogram has 2 sets of parallel lines. Which 2-D shape is a parallelogram?	C
3.	An irregular shape doesn't follow any set pattern. Which shape is irregular?	A
(i)	Questions 4 to 7 are about Caitlin's favorite foods. Read their names. Caitlin doesn't know their names but she can tell you the 3-D shapes that make them. Listen to her description, then write the food she is describing.	
4.	Yesterday she had the food that is a cylinder. Which food is this?	licorice
5.	At recess she likes to eat the food that is a sphere. Write its name.	orange
6.	Sometimes she finishes her meal with the food that is a cone. Write its name.	carrot
7.	Last night she ate the food that is made up of a cylinder and a sphere. Write its name.	mushroom
(i)	Write the letter that matches your answer for questions 8 to 14. The letters and their matching numbers are shown on your sheet. Use the pictures on your sheet to help work them out.	
8.	Elizabeth and Margaret share 4 candies between them. How many will each girl get? Write the letter that matches your answer.	S
9.	Alanna has 8 marbles to put into 2 marble bags. She wants the same number in each bag. How many can she put in each bag? Write the letter that matches your answer.	H
10.	Tim arranged his 12 tin soldiers into 2 equal-sized rows. How many soldiers in each row? Write the letter that matches your answer.	A
11.	The cafeteria table at school seats 20 children. The same number of people sit on the right side as the left side. How many people sit on either side? Write the letter that matches your answer.	R
12.	Luke wants to share 6 cupcakes between Ben and Joshua. How many cupcakes would each of his 2 friends get? Write the letter that matches your answer.	I
13.	A zookeeper has to share 14 bananas between 2 gorillas. How many bananas would each gorilla get? Write the letter that matches your answer.	N
14.	Farmer McGurgle has 10 pumpkin seeds. He thinks it would be nice to plant them in 2 equal rows. How many pumpkin plants would be in each row? Write the letter that matches your answer.	G
	The letters should read "sharing" when put together.	
15.	Look at the cakes on your sheet. Cake "A" has 3 of its 10 slices frosted. As a fraction we write this as 3 over 10. Another way we can write it is as a decimal. As a decimal it is written 0.3.	
	Cake "B" has 5 of its 10 slices frosted. As a fraction we write this as 5 over 10. Another way we can write it is as a decimal. As a decimal it is written 0.5.	
	Cake "C" has 7 of its 10 slices frosted. As a fraction we write this as 7 over 10. Another way we can write it is as a decimal. As a decimal it is written 0.7.	
	Cake "D" has 9 of its 10 slices frosted. Can you write this as fraction?	$^9/_{10}$
16.	Can you write this as a decimal?	0.9
	Numbers to the left of the decimal point stand for whole things. The column to the right of the decimal point stands for parts of a whole.	
(i)	Use the hundreds chart to work out the last 4 questions. You might be able to do them without the chart if you understand the pattern.	
17.	Julie had 61 marbles and found 10 more under the sofa cushions. How many altogether?	71
18.	Anita ate 56 raisins, had a drink, then ate another 10 raisins. How many raisins did she eat altogether?	66
19.	There are 43 children in the Tiny Tots Club. Ten new members joined. How many in the club now?	53
20.	There are 89 ants in Anna Ant's nest. One fine morning, 10 more ants hatched. How many ants are in the nest now?	99

1. _____   6. _____   11. _____   16. _____

2. _____   7. _____   12. _____   17. _____

3. _____   8. _____   13. _____   18. _____

4. _____   9. _____   14. _____   19. _____

5. _____   10. _____   15. _____   20. _____

1–3   trapezoid   parallelogram   irregular shape

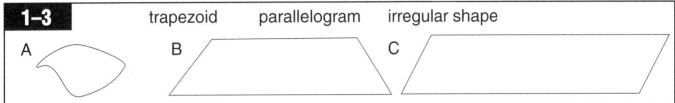

A   B   C

4–7   licorice   mushroom   carrot   orange   **8–14**

CODE	
2 = S	3 = I
6 = A	5 = G
4 = H	7 = N
10 = R	8 = P

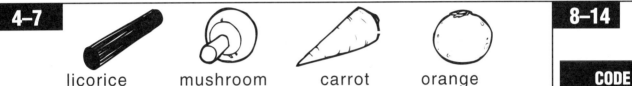

8

10

11

9

12

13

14

15–16

A= $\qquad$ fraction = $3/10$ decimal = 0.3

B = $\qquad$ fraction = $5/10$ decimal = 0.5

C = $\qquad$ fraction = $7/10$ decimal = 0.7

D = $\qquad$ fraction =   decimal =

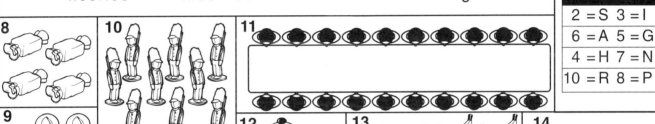

17–20

1	2	3	4	5	6	7	8	9	10
11	12	13	14	15	16	17	18	19	20
21	22	23	24	25	26	27	28	29	30
31	32	33	34	35	36	37	38	39	40
41	42	43	44	45	46	47	48	49	50
51	52	53	54	55	56	57	58	59	60
61	62	63	64	65	66	67	68	69	70
71	72	73	74	75	76	77	78	79	80
81	82	83	84	85	86	87	88	89	90
91	92	93	94	95	96	97	98	99	100

Activity

Draw a space alien made up of irregular shapes on the back of this page.

BLAST 25

Number	Question and Discussion	Answer
	Look at the 12 one-dollar coins on your sheet. They are to be shared equally among Jazmin, Sarah, Michelle and Rachel.	
1.	How much will each girl get?	$3.00
	Listen to the clues. Cross off the numbers that don't belong when you hear a clue. See if you can find the mystery number.	
2.	• I am between 10 and 16. (Discuss which numbers can be eliminated as a result of this clue.)	
	• I am not an even number.	
	• I am more than a dozen.	
	• I am less than the number of days in a two weeks.	
	• What number am I?	13
3.	Estimate the temperature in the classroom right now.	teacher
4.	Jason, Nicholas and Alex each get $5.00 allowance a week from their parents. How much does it cost their parents every week?	$15.00
5.	When she went shopping, Carmen bought a book for $5.00 and a geometry set for $7.00. How much did these cost her altogether?	$12.00
6.	Dad bought $10.00 worth of gas. He paid with a $20.00 bill. How much change did he get?	$10.00
7.	Look at the cake on your sheet. It is cut into 10 slices and 3 are frosted. Choose the fraction that tells you the amount frosted.	$^3/_{10}$
8.	Choose the decimal that tells you the amount frosted.	0.3
9.	The water is 2 degrees below boiling. Choose the answer that tells its temperature. Use the "degrees Celsius" abbreviation when you write your answer.	98°C
10.	Close your eyes and count to estimate the number of seconds between when I say "start" and "stop." Your answer should end in 0 or 5.	teacher
	Allow the stopwatch to run for 50 seconds.	
	Choose a child from the class.	
11.	Estimate this person's height within 20 cm.	teacher
12.	Rebecca bought $5.00 worth of stamps. She paid with a $20.00 bill. How much change did she get?	$15.00
(i)	The next 2 questions are about Fido's kennel and 3 paths he can take to his bone. Use letters to answer the questions.	
13.	Which is the shortest path to Fido's bone?	B
14.	Which is the longest path to his bone?	C
(i)	The next 3 questions are about the 3 corners or "angles." Say the angle words on your sheet after me.	
15.	Which "angle" or "corner" is a "sharp" or "acute" angle?	B
16.	Which "angle" or "corner" is a "blunt" or "obtuse" angle?	C
17.	Which "angle" or "corner" is a "right angle"?	A
	Discuss possible derivation of this term. Ask children which buildings would probably fall down. (Y and Z) X would remain standing because its walls were built at the "right angle."	
(i)	Match the instrument names with their uses. Write the words to answer questions 18 to 20.	
18.	Which would you use to measure a line on your sheet?	ruler
19.	Which would you use to measure a trip in the car?	odometer
20.	What do you use to weigh yourself?	bathroom scale

Additional Material Needed

Room thermometer, stopwatch, something to measure child's height

1. _____   6. _____   11. _____   16. _____

2. _____   7. _____   12. _____   17. _____

3. _____   8. _____   13. _____   18. _____

4. _____   9. _____   14. _____   19. _____

5. _____   10. _____   15. _____   20. _____

1

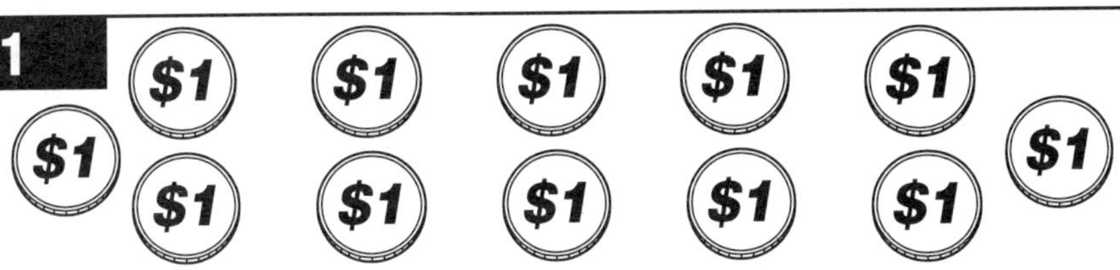

$1 $1 $1 $1 $1
$1
$1 $1 $1 $1 $1 $1

Jazmin   Sarah

Michelle   Rachel

2

8 9 10 11 12 13 14 15 16 17 18

7–8

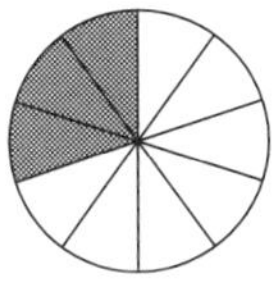

Fraction	$3/_7$	$10/_3$	$3/_{10}$
Decimal	3.0	0.10	0.3

9

100°C   102°C   99°C   98°C

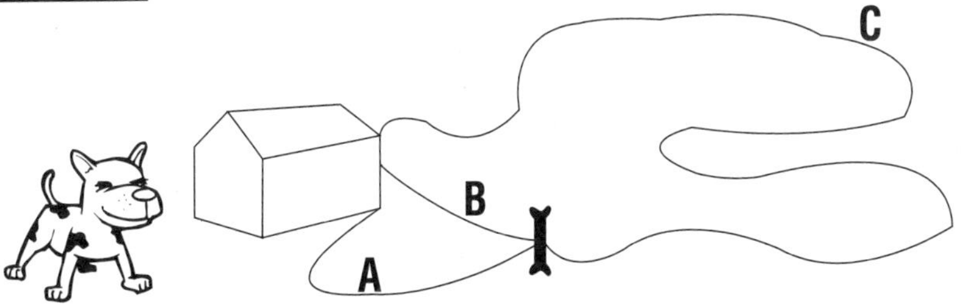

15–17

acute angle

obtuse angle

right angle

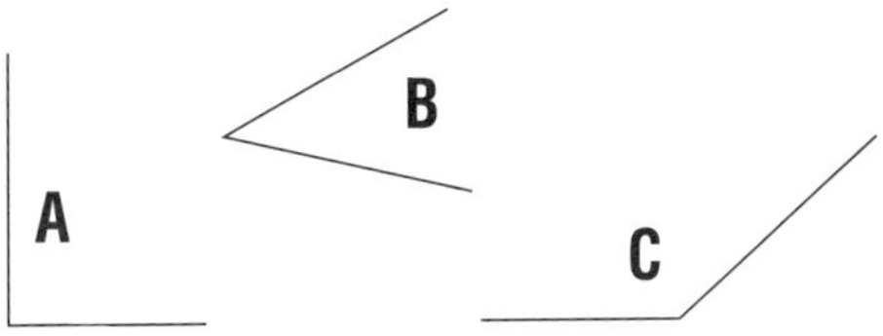

A   B   C

13–14

C
B
A

Color the 2 buildings that would probably fall down.

The remaining building is built with the "right" angles.

X   Y   Z

18–20

thermometer   bathroom scale   weighbridge   odometer   ruler

Activity

1. Draw a shape with more than 5 right angles.

BLAST 26

Number	Question and Discussion	Answer
1.	Complete the symmetrical shape on your sheet to form a letter of the alphabet.	W
ⓘ	Look at the picture of a cake on your sheet. The cake is cut into 10 pieces and 1 piece has frosting on it.	
2.	Choose the fraction on your sheet that tells the amount of cake with frosting.	$^1/_{10}$
3.	Now choose the decimal that tells the amount of frosting.	0.1
4.	Add a horizontal line to the shape on the answer line to make a capital letter.	F or T
ⓘ	The next 5 questions relate to the graph on your sheet. The graph shows the types of cars owned by some families. Each graph space stands for 2 families.	
5.	How many families own sports cars?	4
6.	How many families own sedans?	5
7.	Which car is owned by the biggest number of families?	minivan
8.	Which car is owned by the smallest number of families?	convertible
9.	How many cars are owned altogether by the families?	31
10.	Look at the list of capital letters on your sheet. Write any capital that has 2 or more oblique lines in it.	A, K, M, V, X, Y
11.	If the 3 little pigs each had 5 apples for lunch, how many apples did they eat altogether?	15
12.	What year is it this year?	teacher
13.	What year was it last year?	teacher
14.	What year will it be next year?	teacher
15.	If you flip a coin, which result is most likely: heads, tails, or either equally likely?	either
ⓘ	Match the nets with their names for questions 16 to 18.	
16.	Which net is a pentagonal prism?	C
17.	Which net is a square pyramid?	A
18.	Which net is a triangular prism?	B
19.	Is the mass (weight) of a ton of lead heavier, lighter, or the same as that of a ton of feathers?	the same – both weigh a ton
20.	There are 5 birds, 2 goldfish and 3 dogs in the pet shop. How many legs is this altogether?	22

Activity Answers

1. 9:55, 10:05, 7:30, 4:15, 10:10, 11:25

1. _____ V   6. _____   11. _____   16. _____

2. _____   7. _____   12. _____   17. _____

3. _____   8. _____   13. _____   18. _____

4. _____   9. _____   14. _____   19. _____

5. _____   10. _____   15. _____   20. _____

2–3

fraction =	$\frac{1}{9}$	$\frac{1}{10}$	$\frac{11}{10}$	$\frac{10}{1}$
decimal =	0.9	0.01	1.0	0.1

5–9

sports car						
sedan						
minivan						
convertible						
truck						
station wagon						

= 2 families

10

A B C D E F G H I J K L M N O P Q R S T U V W X Y Z

15

heads   tails   either

16–18

pentagonal prism

square pyramid

triangular prism

A

B

C

19

heavier   lighter   the same

a ton of lead   a ton of feathers

20

5 birds   2 goldfish   3 dogs

Activity

1. Write the times on the digital clocks.

"nine fifty-five"   "ten-oh-five"   "seven-thirty"   "four-fifteen"   "ten-ten"   "eleven twenty-five"

BLAST 27

Number	Question and Discussion	Answer
1.	About how long would it take a good runner at a competition to run 100 meters? Choose from the times on your sheet.	15 seconds

Nine out of ten slices of the cake on your sheet are frosted.

2.	Choose the fraction for this amount.	$^9/_{10}$
3.	Choose the decimal for this amount.	0.9
4.	Look at the capital letters on your sheet. Write any capital that has 2 horizontal lines in it.	F, Z
5.	Look at the curved line on answer line 5. Add a vertical line to turn it into a capital letter.	D or P

Match the times on your sheet with the following events.

6.	Which time would most probably be breakfast time for a child on a school day?	7:30 a.m.
7.	Which time would most probably be lunchtime for a child on a school day?	12:00 p.m.
8.	At which time would children most likely be starting class for the day?	8:30 a.m.
9.	At which time would children most likely be going home from school?	2:30 p.m.
10.	At which time would children most likely be playing after school?	4:30 p.m.

> *"a.m." stands for "ante meridiem" (Latin for "before noon")*
>
> *"p.m." stands for "post meridiem" (Latin for "after noon")*

11. Draw a dotted vertical line of symmetry on answer line 11.

12. Draw a dotted horizontal line of symmetry on answer line 12.

13. Draw a dotted oblique line of symmetry on answer line 13.

14. Shapes **tessellate** when they fit together without leaving any spaces. Which of the shapes on your sheet tessellate?

squares

15. What number am I? Eliminate numbers from the group on your sheet as I give you clues.
- I am between 20 and 30.
- I am more than 2 dozen.
- I am an odd number.
- I can be shared with no remainder among 5 people.
- What number am I?   25

16.	Write the next number in the pattern on your sheet.	19
17.	Leah threw a bean bag 7 meters short of 20 meters. How far did she throw it? Count on the number line on your sheet to check your answer.	13 m
18.	Alan started doing his homework at 5 o'clock in the afternoon. He worked for two hours. At what time did he finish?	7:00 p.m.
19.	Amanda went swimming at 4 o'clock for two hours. At what time did she finish?	6:00

Choose a child from the class.

20.	Estimate this person's height.	teacher

Additional Material Needed

Something to measure child's height

Activity Answers

2. (a) $^1/_{10}$, 0.1   (b) $^2/_{10}$, 0.2   (c) $^3/_{10}$, 0.3   (d) $^5/_{10}$, 0.5   (e) $^4/_{10}$, 0.4

(f) $^6/_{10}$, 0.6   (g) $^8/_{10}$, 0.8   (h) $^9/_{10}$, 0.9

1. _____   6. _____   11. _____   16. _____

2. _____   7. _____   12. _____   17. _____

3. _____   8. _____   13. _____   18. _____

4. _____   9. _____   14. _____   19. _____

5. _____   10. _____   15. _____   20. _____

1	2 seconds
	15 seconds
	1 minute

2–3

fraction = $\frac{1}{9}$ $\frac{1}{10}$ $\frac{9}{1}$ $\frac{9}{10}$

decimal = 0.9   9.1   9.0   9.9

4 A B C D E F G H I J K L M N O P Q R S T U V W X Y Z

6–10 8:30 a.m.   7:30 a.m.   12:00 p.m.   2:30 p.m.   4:30 p.m.   9:30 p.m.

14 square   circle

15 20 21 22 23 24 25 26 27 28 29 30

16 4, 7, 10, 13, 16, _____

17 | 1 | 2 | 3 | 4 | 5 | 6 | 7 | 8 | 9 | 10 | 11 | 12 | 13 | 14 | 15 | 16 | 17 | 18 | 19 | 20 |

Activity

1. **Tessellations**

   If shapes fit together without leaving any spaces they are said to **tessellate**.

   The hexagon tessellates. Bees use this shape when they build their honey combs.

   Use a ruler to help Belinda Bee finish building her hive.
   One hexagonal cell has already been built.

2. **Decimal**: Decimals are another way of writing tenths.
   The **decimal point** separates whole numbers and decimal fraction amounts. Write the fraction and then the decimal fraction for the amount of cake with frosting.

   (a) fraction = $\frac{1}{10}$ decimal = 0.1   (b) fraction = _____   decimal = _____

   (c) fraction = _____   decimal = _____   (d) fraction = _____   decimal = _____

   (e) fraction = _____   decimal = _____   (f) fraction = _____   decimal = _____

   (g) fraction = _____   decimal = _____   (h) fraction = _____   decimal = _____

BLAST 28

Number	Question and Discussion	Answer
1.	How many is 9 minus 3?	6
2.	How many is 90 minus 30?	60
	Discuss the pattern.	
3.	Jeff finished piano practice at 4:00 p.m. He had practiced for 2 straight hours. At what time had he started?	2:00 p.m.
(i)	Poor little Cynthia is lost. It is her first day at Happy Hectares Elementary School and she doesn't really know her way to the classroom. It is at position D on your diagram. Write where she finished, following each set of directions. On each occasion she begins at the front door.	
4.	The first time she turned right, then left, then right. Which room did she come to?	F
5.	Oops! Wrong room! Back to the front door. This time she turned left, then left. Which room did she come to?	A
6.	Oops! Wrong one again. This time she turned right, then left, then left. Which room did she arrive at?	E
7.	Last try this time. "If I don't find it this time, I'm going home to my mommy!" thinks Cynthia. Okay, here goes the last try! This time she went right, then right. Did she go home?	no
8.	Look at shapes A, B and C on your sheet. Which 2 shapes tessellate?	A and C
9.	What number am I? Eliminate numbers as clues are given.	
	• I am between 1 and 10.	
	• If you share me between 2 people, there is a remainder.	
	• I am less than the number of legs a spider has.	
	• I am more than the number of legs a horse has.	
	• I am more than the number of days in a school week.	
	• What number am I?	7
10.	In the diagram of a cake, 8 out of 10 slices are frosted. Which fraction stands for this amount?	$^8/_{10}$
11.	Which decimal stands for this amount?	0.8
12.	Look at the long date written on the board. Write this in short form on answer line 12.	teacher
13.	Write 17 using tally marks.	ℍ ℍ ℍ ‖
14.	Choose the time on your sheet that stands for 1 minute to 10.	9:59
15.	Choose the time on your sheet that stands for 2 minutes past the hour of noon.	12:02
16.	How many minutes in 1 hour? Write the abbreviation for minutes after your answer.	60 min.
17.	How many minutes in half an hour? Write the abbreviation for minutes after your answer.	30 min.
18.	How many minutes in one and a half hours? Write the abbreviation for minutes after your answer.	90 min.
19.	What year will it be next year?	teacher
20.	Estimate the temperature in the classroom right now. Write the "degrees Celsius" abbreviation as part of your answer.	teacher

Additional Material Needed

Long date written on board, room thermometer

Activity Answers

1.   (a) Bank   (b) Toy store   (c) News Stand   (d) Fruit Store   (e) Supermarket   (f) Bakery
       (g) Drugstore   (h) Video Store

1. _____ 6. _____ 11. _____ 16. _____

2. _____ 7. _____ 12. _____ 17. _____

3. _____ 8. _____ 13. _____ 18. _____

4. _____ 9. _____ 14. _____ 19. _____

5. _____ 10. _____ 15. _____ 20. _____

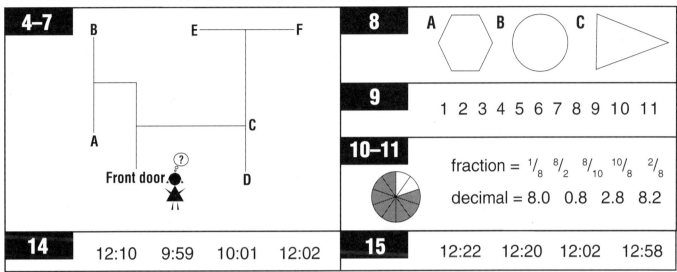

Activity

1. Look at the plan of downtown on your sheet. You are going to see where Tanita went shopping. Write answers on the lines. Begin at the entrance.

(a) First she goes 1 right and 1 up.

Where is she? _____

(b) From here she goes 1 right and 2 up.

Where is she now? _____

(c) Next she goes 1 right and 2 down.

Where is she now? _____

(d) Next she goes 1 right.

Where is she now? _____

(e) From here she goes 2 up and 1 left.

Where is she? _____

(f) Next she goes 1 left and 1 down. Where is she now? _____

(g) She then goes 2 down and 1 right. Where is she? _____

(h) Finally she goes home. Which shop didn't she visit? _____

		Store	Super-market	Video Store
			Bakery	
	Bank		Newsstand	Fruit Store
			Drugstore	

Entrance

BLAST 29

Number	Question and Discussion	Answer
1.	Look at the shapes A, B and C on your sheet. Which 2 tessellate?	B and C
2.	What number am I? Eliminate numbers as the clues are given.	
	• I am between 18 and 30.	
	• I am made up of 2 different digits.	
	• I am not an odd number.	
	• I am less than 2 dozen.	
	• What number am I?	20
3.	Muhammed went to the pool at 3 o'clock in the afternoon and trained for two and a half hours. What time was showing on his waterproof digital watch when he finished?	5:30

ⓘ The next 5 questions are about a sandwich eating contest between Kenneth and Renee. The "x" stands for the number of sandwiches eaten by Kenneth and the "o" stands for the number of sandwiches eaten by Renee.

4.	How many sandwiches did Kenneth eat on Saturday?	8
5.	How many sandwiches did Renee eat on Monday?	6
6.	On which day did indigestion strike Kenneth? Write the abbreviation.	Mon.
7.	How many sandwiches did Kenneth eat altogether?	12
8.	Who was the champion sandwich eater?	Renee
	Discuss: What critical tactical blunder may Kenneth have made? (Too enthusiastic at the beginning of the contest.)	
9.	25 out of 100 slices of the cake on your sheet have frosting. Choose the fraction that stands for this.	$^{25}/_{100}$
10.	100 plus 38 is 138. How many is 99 plus 38?	137
	99 is 1 less than 100, so the answer will be 1 less than 100 plus 38.	
11.	How many is 10 minus 8?	2
12.	How many is 100 minus 80?	20

ⓘ The next 5 questions relate to the time line shown on your sheet. The time line tells about a typical day for Jazmin.

13.	At what time did she have a bad dream?	4:00 a.m.
14.	When did she have breakfast?	8:00 a.m.
15.	Half an hour after eating her lunch (which took her about 5 seconds) she played tag. At what time did she play tag?	1:00 p.m.
16.	Volleyball practice finished at 5:00 o'clock in the afternoon. How long did it go for?	1 hr
17.	Jazmin stopped snoring loudly and settled into a comfortable sleep at midnight. For how many hours was she snoring loudly?	3 hrs
18.	Which capital letter between P and T in the alphabet is made up of an oblique, vertical and curved line?	R
19.	The children were having fun making 2-D shapes. They had a piece of rope and 8 sticks. The shapes A, B, C and D are the shapes they made. They used the rope to make an ellipse. Which shape is the ellipse?	C
20.	They used all the sticks to make an octagon. Which shape is the octagon?	B

Activity Answers

1. (a) C   (b) 3   (c) 6   (d) B   (e) 4   (f) 8

1. _____   6. _____   11. _____   16. _____

2. _____   7. _____   12. _____   17. _____

3. _____   8. _____   13. _____   18. _____

4. _____   9. _____   14. _____   19. _____

5. _____   10. _____   15. _____   20. _____

1

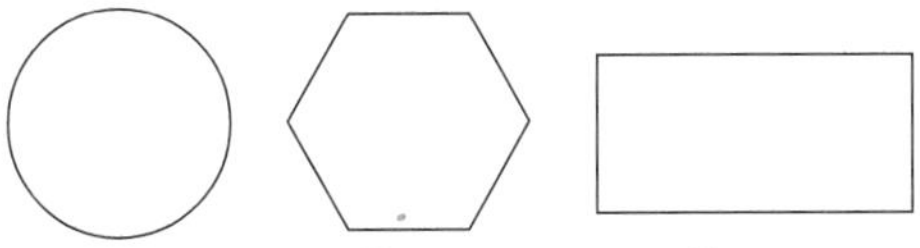

A   B   C

2

20	21	22	23	24	25	26	27
28	29	30	31	32	33	34

4–8

X = Kenneth   O = Renee

Saturday
X X X X X X X
O O O O

Sunday
X X X X
O O O O O O

Monday
O O O O O O

9

$\frac{1}{25}$

$\frac{25}{10}$

$\frac{25}{100}$

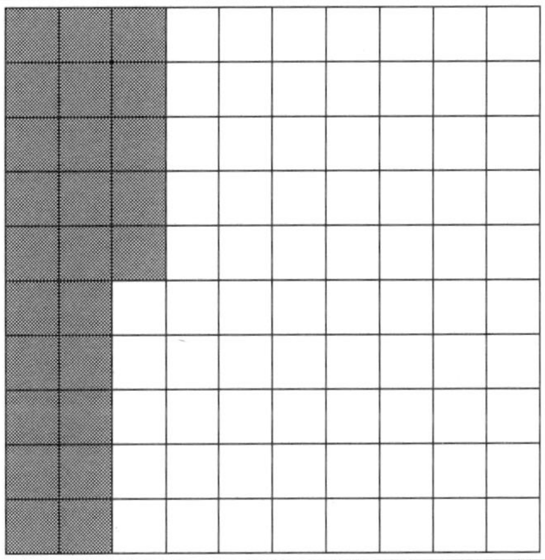

13–17

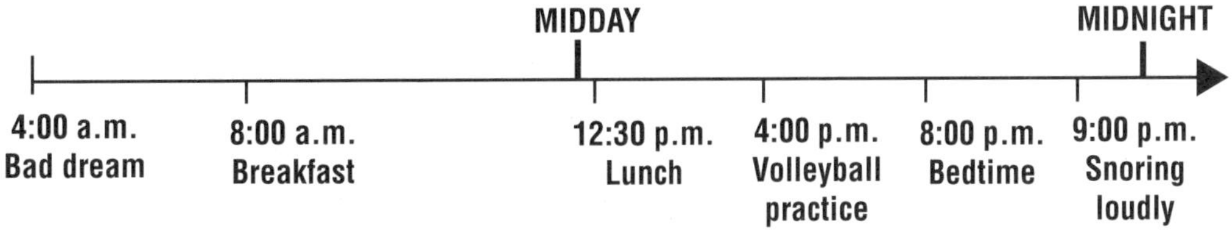

MIDDAY   MIDNIGHT

4:00 a.m.   8:00 a.m.   12:30 p.m.   4:00 p.m.   8:00 p.m.   9:00 p.m.
Bad dream   Breakfast   Lunch   Volleyball   Bedtime   Snoring
                                       practice   loudly

18

P   Q   R   S   T

19–20   octagon   ellipse

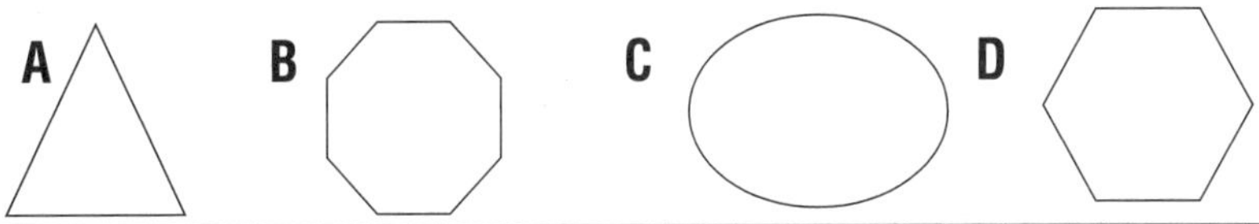

A   B   C   D

Activity

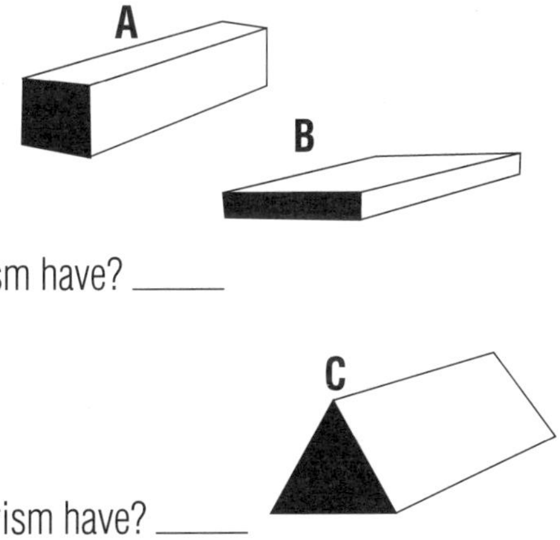

1. Look at the pictures representing solid shapes on your sheet.

    (a) Which shape represents a triangular prism? _____

    (b) How many sides does a triangle have? _____

    (c) How many corners (or vertices, or points) does the triangular prism have? _____

    (d) Which shape represents a rectangular prism? _____

    (e) How many sides does a rectangle have? _____

    (f) How many corners (or vertices, or points) does the rectangular prism have? _____

A

B

C

Books Available from World Teachers Press®

MATH

A Blast of Math
Grades 3-4, 4-5, 5-6, 6-7

Math Word Puzzles
Grades 5-8

Mastergrids for Math
Elementary Resource

Essential Facts and Tables
Grades 3-10

Math Puzzles Galore
Grades 4-8

Practice Math
Grades 4, 5, 6, 7

Math Speed Tests
Grades 1-3, 3-6

Problem Solving with Math
Grades 2-3, 4-5, 6-8

Math Through Language
Grades 1-2, 2-3, 3-4

Exploring Measurement
Grades 2-3, 3-4, 5-6

Chance, Statistics & Graphs
Grades 1-3, 3-5

Step Into Tables
Elementary

Problem Solving Through Investigation
Grades 5-8, 7-10

The Early Fraction Book
Grades 3-4

The Fraction Book
Grades 5-8

It's About Time
Grades 2-3, 4-5

Do It Write Math
Grades 2-3

Mental Math Workouts
Grades 4-6, 5-7, 6-8, 7-9

Math Grid Games
Grades 4-8

High Interest Mathematics
Grades 5-8

Math Homework Assignments
Grades 2, 3, 4, 5, 6, 7

Visual Discrimination
Grades 1-12

Active Math

Math Enrichment
Grades 4-7

Time Tables Challenge

30 Math Games
PreK-1

Early Skills Series:
Addition to Five, Counting and
Recognition to Five, Cutting Activities,
Early Visual Skills

Spatial Relations
Grades 1-2, 3-4, 5-6

High Interest Geometry
Grades 5-8

Money Matters
Grades 1, 2, 3

LANGUAGE ARTS

Multiple-Choice Comprehension
Grades 2-3, 4-5, 6-7

My Desktop Dictionary
Grades 2-5

Spelling Essentials
Grades 3-10

Reading for Detail
Grades 4-5, 6-7

Writing Frameworks
Grades 2-3, 4-5, 6-7

Spelling Success
Grades 1, 2, 3, 4, 5, 6, 7

My Junior Spelling Journal
Grades 1-2

My Spelling Journal
Grades 3-6

Cloze Encounters
Grades 1-2, 3-4, 5-6

Comprehension Lifters
1, 2, 3, 4

Grammar Skills
Grades 2-3, 4-5, 6-8

*Vocabulary Development through
Dictionary Skills*
Grades 3-4, 5-6, 7-8

Recipes for Readers
Grades 3-6

Step Up To Comprehension
Grades 2-3, 4-5, 6-8

Cloze
Grades 2-3, 4-5, 6-8

Cloze in on Language
Grades 3-5, 4-6, 5-7, 6-8

Initial Sounds Fold-Ups

Phonic Sound Cards

Early Activity Phonics

Activity Phonics

Early Phonics in Context

Phonics in Context

Build-A-Reader

Communicating
Grades 5-6

Oral Language
Grades 2-3, 4-5, 6-8

Listen! Hear!
Grades 1-2, 3-4, 5-6

Phonic Fold-Ups

Word Study
Grades 2-3, 4-5, 6-7, 7-8

Draw to a Cloze
Grades 5-8

Classical Literature
Grades 3-4, 5-6, 5-8

High Interest Vocabulary
Grades 5-8

Literacy Lifters
1, 2, 3 ,4

Look! Listen! Think!
Grades 2-3, 4-5, 6-7

Teach Editing
Grades 2-3, 3-4, 5-6

Proofreading and Editing
Grades 3-4, 4-8, 7-8

High Interest Language
Grades 5-8

Comprehend It!
Grades 1-3, 4-5, 6-8

Comprehension for Young Readers

Language Skill Boosters
Grades 1, 2, 3, 4, 5, 6, 7

Phonic Charts

Vocabulary Sleuths
Grades 5-7, 6-9

Early Theme Series:
Bears, Creepy Crawlies, The Sea

Phonics in Action Series:
Initial Sounds, Final Consonant
Sounds, Initial Blends and
Digraphs, Phonic Pictures

OTHERS

Exploring Change
Grades 3-4, 5-6, 7-8

*Ancient Egypt, Ancient Rome,
Ancient Greece*
Grades 4-7

Australian Aboriginal Culture
Grades 3-4, 5-6, 7-8

Reading Maps
Grades 2-3, 4-5, 6-8

The Music Book
Grades 4-8

Mapping Skills
Grades 2-3, 3-4, 5-6

Introducing The Internet

Internet Theme Series:
Sea, The Solar System,
Endangered Species

Art Media

Visit us at:
www.worldteacherspress.com
for further information and free
sample pages.